CLASSICS

IN THE THEORY

OF CHEMICAL

COMBINATION

Classics
in the
Theory of Chemical Combination

CLASSICS OF SCIENCE SERIES

under the General Editorship of

Gerald Holton

Professor of Physics, Harvard University

Classics of Science, Volume I

Classics
in the
Theory of Chemical Combination

Edited by

O. THEODOR BENFEY

Department of Chemistry
Earlham College

DOVER PUBLICATIONS, INC.
NEW YORK

Published in Canada by General Publishing Company, Ltd., 30 Lesmill Road, Don Mills, Toronto, Ontario.

Published in the United Kingdom by Constable and Company, Limited, 10 Orange Street, London, W.C. 2.

Classics in the Theory of Chemical Combination (Volume I in the Dover "Classics of Science" series), contains nine papers published for the first time in collected form by Dover Publications, Inc., in 1963.

This volume also contains a new Preface, Epilogue and notes by O. Theodor Benfey.

The editors and publisher are grateful to the Chemistry Library of Columbia University for making certain of these papers available for reproduction purposes.

Library of Congress Catalog Card Number: 63-17897

Manufactured in the United States of America.

Dover Publications, Inc.
180 Varick Street,
New York 14, N.Y.

General Editor's Preface

This volume, together with a few others that are being published in this new series at about the same time, inaugurates a publishing program entitled *Classics of Science*. Each volume is to be a collection of the fundamental essays and other basic original articles in a certain field of science, presented in the sequence of its development, together with an introduction, commentary, and clarifying notes by the scholar responsible for the selection of the papers. All areas of science are to be included as the series grows. The titles of volumes commissioned for early completion range from *The Discovery of Radioactivity and Transmutations* to *The Theory of Evolution (1830 to Modern Genetic Theory)*. Thus, in time, we shall have here a convenient network of roads to take us to the usually inaccessible sources of the great rivers of science, through its widely visible mountain ranges, its renowned battlefields, and its little-known but nevertheless choice vineyards.

The articles will follow the original texts verbatim, and (with rare and clearly marked exceptions) will be printed in full rather than in excerpt or in edited and abbreviated versions; they may therefore be used in lieu of the original publications. Foreign-language articles will be carefully translated. In short, both the interested layman and the historian or scientist should feel assured that he is reading these documents as they were intended to be read, and in the version in which they made their original contribution.

Some of these aims are similar to those of a distinguished German series of republications, begun in 1889 under the direction of the chemist and philosopher, Wilhelm Ostwald, and reaching over 400 titles before it was discontinued. There are, however, important distinctions between these two series. Ostwald's series was composed of republications of single essays, whereas here each book sets out each of the several essays in the context of others, in order to trace the development of the whole field. Hence there will be more connective commentary in this series, and, most importantly, the commentary can now benefit from advances made in the last three-quarters of a century, both in science and in historical scholarship.

Still, many of the aims cited in the original announcement of Ostwald's *Klassiker der exakten Wissenschaften* are again applicable:

> The great progress which the sciences have made in our time, as is generally acknowledged, is in good measure owing to the cultivation and wide application of teaching methods such as demonstration lectures and laboratories. These arrangements are indeed very successful in imparting knowledge of the present state of science. But some of the most eminent persons with widest vision have frequently felt compelled to point out a deficiency that mars all too often our contemporary scientific education. This is the absence of a sense of history, and the lack of knowledge concerning those great contributions on which the edifice of science rests.
>
> Although few instructors in scientific subjects would fail to make reference to those foundations when the occasion arises, such references remain, nevertheless, generally ineffective because the source materials of science are rarely accessible. They can be obtained only in the larger libraries, and then only in single copy, so that the student is all too easily discouraged from pursuing the lead.
>
> This lack is to be remedied through the publication of the *Klassiker der exakten Wissenschaften*. In convenient format and at reasonable prices, the seminal publications of all the exact sciences will be made available to instructors and students alike. The publisher hopes to create thereby both a teaching aid that gives life and depth to the study of science, as well as a significant research tool; for in those fundamental writings lie not only the seeds which have, in the meantime, developed and borne fruit, but also unnumbered other leads that await development. To those whose study and research lie in the sciences, these works offer an inexhaustible source for stimulation and for the advancement of ideas.

Today, no less than when these words were written, the proper orientation of science is toward the future. Yet, the uses of the scientific past are also becoming clearer—not the least being the continued application of Maxwell's memorable dictum on the didactic value of the study of historical accounts and of original works in science, found in the preface to the *Treatise on Electricity and Magnetism*: "It is of great advantage to the student of any subject to read the original memoirs on that subject, for science is always most completely assimilated when it is in the nascent state. . . ."

This series of connected essays on single topics of science will help us to remember that in the development of each field the overriding characteristic of scientific growth is its continuity. If science as done today is so good, it is to a large extent because science as done in the past was so good.

Cambridge, Mass.
September, 1962

Gerald Holton
Jefferson Laboratory
Harvard University

Acknowledgment

The editor of this volume wishes to express his gratitude to the Harvard University Press for permission to use parts of the translation of Kekulé's "Ueber die Constitution und die Metamorphosen der chemischen Verbindungen und über die chemische Natur des Kohlenstoffs" in *A Sourcebook in Chemistry* by H. M. Leicester and H. S. Klickstein; to the Royal Society of Edinburgh for permission to use the translation of A. S. Couper's short paper, "On a New Chemical Theory," which appeared in Alembic Club Reprint No. 21, entitled *On a New Chemical Theory and Researches on Salicylic Acid* (Edinburgh, 1953), pp. 9–13; and to the editors of the *Journal of the American Chemical Society* for permission to quote, in the Epilogue, parts of G. N. Lewis's paper, "The Atom and the Molecule," appearing in the *Journal* in 1916, pp. 762–785.

I am indebted also to Erwin Hiebert of the History of Science Department at the University of Wisconsin for drawing my attention to two Dutch studies on valence, *Het Ontstaan van het Begrip Valentie*, by A. C. W. Roodvoets (Bosch und Zoon, Utrecht, 1934), and *De Ontwikkeling van het Begrip Valentie*, by T. R. A. Beukema (Luctor et Emergo, Leiden, 1935), and for making these available to me.

This volume was prepared during a summer's sojourn in the peaceful surroundings of Gambier, Ohio. My thanks go to Eric Graham of the Chemistry Department of Kenyon College for providing me that opportunity. I owe thanks to Gerald Holton of Harvard University for suggesting the preparation of this volume and for his continued help and encouragement; to the National Science Foundation for a grant in support of the early researches which made possible the acceptance of the present assignment; to Lucille Rice and her staff at Earlham College for preparation of the manuscript; to Stephen A. Benfey for help in the reading of proof; and to Rachel Benfey for help in many ways.

O. T. B.

Contents

List of Illustrations

Classics

in the

Theory of Chemical Combination

Introduction

As contrasted with the general and unlimited cohesive tendency which we know as gravitation, the question of valence is the question of elective and limited affinity. The broader question was settled first, long before enough chemistry was known to permit a clear recognition of valence as a further problem of cohesion in nature.

It is instructive to note briefly the fate of quantitative explanations in the history of natural philosophy, since the valence of an element as understood in the middle of the nineteenth century could be expressed simply by a number. The concept would have delighted the Pythagoreans, for Pythagoras and his school had developed a conception of the universe based almost exclusively on the properties of integers. Their conception collapsed, it is said, on the rock of irrational numbers, and the Aristotelian world view became accepted dogma in the Western world.

According to this view, mathematical perfection resided in the outer spheres of the heavenly bodies. Mathematical astronomy thus remained a possibility, but the chances of finding mathematical laws on earth were slim indeed. The annoying wanderings of the planets forced on astronomers the necessity of attaching epicycles to the geocentric spheres and further cycles linked to the first attachments. Copernicus could not believe that God's laws were so complicated, and having studied some recently discovered classical writings which seriously proposed the movement of the earth, he proceeded to determine whether a different center of reference would lead to a simpler mathematical ordering. Copernicus did not see in his proposals a major break with his cultural background. He regarded his contribution as helping to make the laws of the universe the simplest and most perfect possible, in line with the belief in the rationality and perfection of God and in the Aristotelian criteria of celestial motion.

The impact of the Copernican view on science was of course profound. With the sun as the center, the earth becomes a planet like the others. The qualitative difference between the earth on the one side and the heavenly bodies on the other disappears. If mathematical laws apply to the planetary motions and, with equal validity, to the movement of the earth around the sun, then mathematical laws may also apply to phenomena on the surface of the earth. The stage was set for the work of Kepler and Galileo.

For Galileo studies of the moon or the phases of Venus were not qualitatively different from studies of the pendulum and of inclined planes. The approach was the same, the kind of results expected were governed by the same outlook. Tycho Brahe and Kepler brought the observation of planetary motion and planetary theory closer to perfection, and, finally, Newton combined the motions of the planets and the laws of falling bodies into one universal law of gravitation. The universe held together.

But there was more to the universe than its oneness. There was, for instance, the bewildering diversity of its material phenomena, its rocks and plants and animals, its processes of growth and decay, of corrosion and combustion, of reactions between some substances and the complete lack of reaction between others. Here one encountered selective cohesion as well as limited cohesion. A piece of iron will rust and continue to rust, up to a certain point. Beyond that point no further combination with the air occurs. The process is complete. Not all chemical changes follow this pattern, but sufficiently many do to attract attention.

During the years 1803 to 1808, John Dalton put forward his atomic theory, emphasizing a quantitative characteristic of the atoms, their weights. All atoms of the same element had the same weight, but the weights of atoms of different elements were different. The determination of atomic weights, whether relative or absolute, turned out to be a harder task than the enunciation of the principle.

Major assumptions had to be made before measured combining weights could yield information concerning relative atomic weights. Dalton made the simplest assumption, that the commonest compound of two elements A and B possessed the formula AB; it was made up of units consisting of an atom of A combined with an atom of B. One of Dalton's early papers is based on the experimental conclusion that one part by weight of hydrogen combines with seven parts by weight of oxygen. According to his axiom of simplicity, the formula of water must be HO; the atomic weights of hydrogen and oxygen must, therefore, be in the ratio of 1 to 7. Dalton was, of course, wrong. The axiom of simplicity is only an imperfect guide and the concept of valence had yet to be developed. Dalton was not aware of the possibility that a given element may have an inherent combining capacity that sought to be satisfied in compound formation. Nor was Berzelius.

Berzelius did not follow Dalton's axiom of simplicity. He developed his formulas according to a number of principles, and often had finally to use his intuition to arrive at a suitable atomic weight. He was quite willing to conceive of whole series of compounds with formulas AB, AB_2, AB_3, ..., A_2B, A_3B, A_4B, ... These obeyed the law of multiple proportions, and Berzelius (1814) convinced himself that even organic compounds could be represented by similar formulas, though these usually would contain the same three or four elements, carbon, hydrogen, oxygen, and nitrogen.

The possibility that only certain of these combinations, A_xB_y, were found in nature or were capable of preparation in the laboratory could only arise after the attempt had been made to prepare a large number of them. The concept of valence is first of all a limiting law. It enunciates that, out of the possibilities predicted by existing laws, only a limited number can in fact be realized. In Whittaker's phrase, it is a "Principle of Impotence," and such a principle can only be developed after repeated and systematic failures to achieve an end previously conceived as possible.

The concept of valence grew in the soil of organic chemistry. Berzelius' electrochemical dualism had a germ of the idea in the sense of the mutual satisfaction of opposite charges. But the charges were in most cases not considered as inherent properties of the parts, but as induced by the proximity of adjacent atoms. The charges were never considered as multiples of some unit. Aluminum sulfate was still assumed to have some residual negative charge, and sodium sulfate, a residual positive charge—else there was no explanation for their union to form alum.

In the early nineteenth century organic chemistry was likened by Friedrich Wöhler (1800–1882) to a jungle. Wöhler himself, by his urea synthesis, supplied a ray of hope. The gulf between inorganic and organic compounds was perhaps not unbridgeable. But the transformation of silver cyanate and ammonium chloride into urea supplied no pattern for others to follow. The paper by Wöhler and Justus Liebig (1803–1873), a translation of which is the first paper in this collection, supplied this pattern. It had been foreshadowed by the work of Joseph Louis Gay-Lussac (1778–1850) on cyanogen compounds[1] and of Jean Baptiste André Dumas (1800–1884) on the derivatives of etherin.[2] Wöhler and Liebig's paper on the benzoyl radical demonstrated a simple connection between an aldehyde, an alcohol, an acid, an amide, an acyl halide, and a cyanide. Benzaldehyde, the oil of bitter almonds,

---

[1] J. L. Gay-Lussac, *Annales de Chimie et de Physique*, *95*, 136, 200 (1815).
[2] J. B. A. Dumas and P. Boullay, *Ann. Chim.*, *37*, 15 (1828).

could be converted into each of these compounds by the use of suitable reagents. Only a small part of the molecule was changed. A major portion, the "benzoyl radical" (C_7H_5O, using present atomic weights), remained intact throughout the transformations.

The demonstration of this fact required considerable experimental skill. Available thermometers could not reach the boiling point of benzaldehyde, and so could not provide the simplest test of the purity of a liquid. The analysis for carbon and hydrogen, by methods largely perfected by Liebig himself, disagreed in the case of benzoic acid with that published by Berzelius. On its correctness, and on that of the formula of the acid deduced from the analysis, rested most of the remaining demonstration.

Berzelius rechecked, and admitted his error. At the end of the Wöhler–Liebig paper, a note by Berzelius was added, voicing his enthusiasm for this new day that had dawned in vegetable chemistry. His enthusiasm had a good reason. The radicals of organic chemists could now be considered the equivalents of the atoms of inorganic chemistry. With that assumption, organic compounds might fit neatly into Berzelius' dualistic scheme; the necessity of introducing a separate force holding organic compounds together might be avoided.

The chlorination of benzaldehyde, according to Wöhler and Liebig's notation, replaced two atoms of hydrogen by two of chlorine. The latter could be replaced by two bromine atoms, by two NH_2 groups, or by two OH groups. The constancy and simplicity of these numerical relations, discovered and rediscovered in countless instances, led finally to the formulation of a principle, *the valence concept*. It took over twenty-five years to formulate it as a general property of atoms.

The Wöhler–Liebig paper supplied a pattern of research in organic chemistry: Seek out the radicals, the units of organic molecules, as they reveal themselves in chemical transformations. There was the hope that the number of radicals was limited as the number of elements was probably limited. Research soon indicated otherwise; there seemed no end to the number of radicals. The main problem soon changed from discovering radicals to organizing them.

While the results of the Wöhler–Liebig paper could easily be fitted into Berzelius' scheme, a parallel development could not. Some candles bleached with chlorine had given off highly irritating vapors at a gathering at the Tuileries. Dumas was asked to investigate the problem. Chlorine, it turned out, had replaced hydrogen in the wax, "volume for volume," or equivalent for equivalent; as

Dumas put it, chlorine atoms were "taking the place of" hydrogen in the hydrocarbon wax.

Berzelius (who must have overlooked the chlorination of benzaldehyde and Gay-Lussac's experiments with HCN and ClCN) could not accept this. By Berzelius' doctrine, electropositive hydrogen could never yield its place to electronegative chlorine; they were too different. Such a substitution would lead to the most fundamental redistribution of atoms in the molecule. Dumas often could find little difference between chlorinated and unchlorinated material, but he bowed before Berzelius, and insisted that he had only expressed a relation between incoming and outgoing chemicals.

His student Auguste Laurent (1807–1853) went much further. In a series of papers he affirmed that the radicals were not fundamentally altered by substitution, that the properties of the molecule were determined more by the geometric *arrangement* of the atoms than by their nature.[3] After further studies, Dumas agreed, publishing his views in the form of his theory of "types."[4] In its extreme form it suggested that any atom can be replaced by any other, the properties of the substance remaining essentially unaltered. This seemed preposterous to some, and in 1840, in an issue of Liebig's *Annalen*, appeared a letter signed S. C. H. Windler (*Schwindler* is the German word for swindler) and purporting to come from Paris, in which it was claimed that by the successive chlorination of manganous acetate a substance containing only chlorine and water was obtained which yet retained all the properties of manganous acetate. Wöhler had sent the letter to Berzelius and Liebig as a joke, without thought of publication. Liebig, the editor, published it, adding an unsigned footnote: "I have just learned that in the shops of London there are already fabrics of spun chlorine, very much in demand in the hospitals and preferred over all others for night caps, drawers, etc."[5]

This conception of the unlimited substitution of any element for any other broke down because of the fact of valence; in modern terms, only an atom whose valence is of the same kind and

---

[3] A. Laurent, *Ann. Chim.*, *61*, 125 (1836); *63*, 377 (1836); *66*, 326 (1837); *Comptes rendus de l'Académie des Sciences*, *10*, 409 (1840); Thèse de Docteur, Paris, 1837.

[4] J. B. A. Dumas, *Annalen der Pharmacie*, *32*, 101 (1839); *Annalen der Chemie und Pharmacie*, *33*, 179 (1840); *C.R. Acad. Sci.*, *8*, 609 (1839).

[5] S. C. H. Windler [F. Wöhler] *Ann.*, *33*, 308 (1840). Translated in G. W. Wheland, *Advanced Organic Chemistry* (2nd ed., New York, John Wiley & Sons, 1949), p. 678; based on the translation of H. B. Friedman, *Journal of Chemical Education*, *7*, 633 (1930).

magnitude can take another's place without changing the geometry of the molecule (with the further restriction often applying that the atoms must be of similar size). If an oxygen atom attached to two different radicals is replaced by chlorine, we now know that two chlorine atoms are needed, each linked to only one other atom. The two parts of the molecule previously held together by oxygen thus fall apart and become constituents of two separate molecules.

The second paper included in the present collection deals with the facts and theories of organic substitution. The author, Auguste Laurent, having been involved in numerous polemics with Berzelius and others, attempted to collect his views and contributions in his *Méthode de Chimie*. It was published posthumously in 1854, and the translation by William Odling (1829–1921) appeared in 1855. The extract which follows begins with the denial that carbon can be substituted by any other element; it proceeds to deny the possibility that chlorine, bromine and hydrogen, on the one hand, are "equivalent" to oxygen, sulfur, selenium, and tellurium, on the other. Each group represents among its own members "equivalent" bodies, defined as "bodies which may replace one another mutually in their combinations, without altering the principal properties of the compounds into which they enter." Later are listed nitrogen, phosphorus, arsenic, and antimony as a further group of equivalent bodies without analogy outside that group.

In the major section, "Theory of Chlorine Substitutions," Laurent surveys the long battle with Berzelius, ending in the latter's oblique admission that in a *certain part* of an organic molecule, the "copula" or hydrocarbon residue, chlorine may take the place of hydrogen without a fundamental alteration of chemical properties. Thus he formulated acetic acid as $C_2H_3 + C_2O_3$; the hydrogen in the copula, C_2H_3, was replaceable by chlorine, forming trichloro-acetic acid, $C_2Cl_3 + C_2O_3$. *How* these molecules were held together when electrochemical properties did not come into play, was not known. The elucidation of the *nature* of valence forces represents essentially the modern chapter in the history of the valence concept. It is discussed in the Epilogue of this volume.

Parallel to and largely independent of the work discussed so far, a second line of research led to important conclusions that were of use in the development of the valence concept. In the third paper, dated 1851, Alexander William Williamson (1824–1904) suggested that an atomic grouping (CO) "holds together" two parts of a molecule which would otherwise fall apart. This conception can be traced back to Liebig's researches on polybasic acids,[6] which in

---

[6] J. Liebig, *Ann.*, *26*, 113 (1838).

turn followed Graham's studies of 1833 concerning the phosphoric acids.[7] Liebig defined a polybasic acid as one from which salts can be prepared containing more than one kind of metal. He recognized that hereby a new tool had been developed for the elucidation of molecular formulas. If tartaric acid can form a sodium potassium tartrate, then the formula for the acid must contain two replaceable hydrogens. For this reason he doubled the currently accepted formula. The criterion was not always successful, as he was unable to isolate a sodium potassium sulfate, and hence concluded that sulfuric acid was monobasic.

During the 1840's, mainly through the persistent efforts of Laurent and Charles Frédéric Gerhardt (1816–1856), the concepts of "equivalent," "atom," and "molecule" were being clarified and a set of atomic weights developed on the basis of Avogadro's hypothesis. Organic molecular formulas rapidly came to agreement with those in use today, and only in the case of some metals were the atomic weights in error. These had to await Cannizzaro's clarification at the Congress of Karlsruhe in 1860.

Laurent classified compounds according to "mechanical types," that is, according to similarities in formulas, irrespective of parallels in their physical or chemical properties. In one table he puts in the first column OHH, OHK, OKK, OEtH, OEtK, OEtEt (Et = Ethyl, C_2H_5); in another the sulfur analogs, SHH, SHK, SKK, etc., in a third SO_4HH, SO_4HK, SO_4KK, SO_4EtH, SO_4EtK, SO_4EtEt; and similarly the sulfite, carbonate, and oxalate derivatives. All could be seen as belonging to the same fundamental "water type" OHH as Thomas Sterry Hunt (1826–1892) pointed out in his commentary.[8] Williamson's statement that certain groups can hold two parts of a molecule together was not an innovation in principle; it was only an explicit statement of what was implied by Laurent's formulas and by Williamson's own classic work on the constitution of ethers.[9] A year earlier Charles Adolphe Wurtz (1817–1884) had developed the "ammonia type"[10] by preparing a series of amines, and to these types Gerhardt added the hydrogen and hydrogen chloride types, HH and HCl. On the basis of these four types, by the substitution of atoms or radicals, Gerhardt and Laurent set up their classification of organic compounds.

---

[7] T. Graham, *Philosophical Transactions of the Royal Society of London*, 253 (1833).

[8] A. Laurent, *Ann. Chim.*, [3], *18*, 266 (1846); excerpts translated with commentary by T. S. Hunt, *American Journal of Science*, [2], *6*, 173 (1848).

[9] A. W. Williamson, *Philosophical Magazine and Journal of Science*, [3], *37*, 350–356 (1850).

[10] C. A. Wurtz, *C.R. Acad. Sci.*, *28*, 223 (1849).

One aspect alone was lacking for the enunciation of the classic valence theory. No one had yet said that water was the *only* type in which oxygen could appear, or else that an atom was limited as to the number of groups that it could hold together. This step was supplied by Edward Frankland (1825–1899) in 1852. Arising out of work aimed at the isolation of organic radicals, an aim which at one time he thought he had achieved, he had accidentally prepared some organometallic compounds. These he then studied systematically and, surveying a large number of related inorganic compounds, he was struck by the "general symmetry of their construction."

> The compounds of nitrogen, phosphorus, antimony, and arsenic especially exhibit the tendency of these elements to form compounds containing three or five equivalents of other elements, and it is in these proportions that their affinities are best satisfied...without offering any hypothesis regarding the cause of this symmetrical grouping of atoms, it is sufficiently evident, from the examples just given, that such a tendency or law prevails, and that, no matter what the character of the uniting atoms may be, the combining-power of the attracting element, if I may be allowed the term, is always satisfied by the same number of these atoms. It was probably a glimpse of the operation of this law amongst the more complex organic groups which led Laurent and Dumas to the enunciation of the theory of types; and had not those distinguished chemists extended their views beyond the point to which they were well supported by then existing facts, had they not assumed that the properties of an organic compound are dependent upon the *position* and not upon the *nature* of its single atoms, that theory would undoubtedly have contributed to the development of the science to a still greater extent than it had already done. Such an assumption could only have been made at a time when the data upon which it was founded were few and imperfect.[11]

This passage appears in the fourth paper of this volume. It is considered the first complete statement of the valence concept, though followers of Kekulé (1829–1896) for a time insisted that the honor should go to the latter, since Frankland used equivalent rather than atomic weights in his argument. Kekulé further differed markedly from Frankland in his insistence that atoms could have only one valence. Kekulé considered ammonium chloride a loose molecular compound of ammonia and hydrogen chloride, a view which for long prevailed against Frankland's position that nitrogen here exhibited a valence of five. The modern view is more complex, involving two types of valence.

Frankland spoke of surveying "inorganic" compounds. The question of the constitution of organic radicals remained untouched. In the years that followed, organic radicals were examined further. Hermann Kolbe (1818–1884), for instance, suggested that acetic

---

[11] E. Frankland, *Phil. Trans.*, *142*, 440–441 (1852).

acid was made up of a methyl radical and two groups containing oxygen, the carbonyl and hydroxyl groups, as they are now called.[12] According to the symbolism of the type theory, acetic acid was later written

$$\left. \begin{array}{l} CH_3 \\ CO \\ H \end{array} \right\} O$$

representing a hydrogen type $\left. \begin{array}{l} H \\ H \end{array} \right\}$ and a water type $\left. \begin{array}{l} H \\ H \end{array} \right\} O$ held together by a "diatomic" (or bivalent) CO group. The type theory permitted the replacement of H in a type by an organic radial.

The problem that remained was the nature of carbon. How was it capable of holding together the enormously complex radicals which appeared in the types? The answer was proposed by Odling, Kekulé, and Couper, and was implied in some of Kolbe's formulas. The time was obviously ripe for analyzing organic radicals down to the constituent atoms.

In the first stage, Odling[13] and Friedrich August Kekulé (1829–1896)[14] suggested the logical extension of Gerhardt's HH, HCl, H_2O, H_3N types to include the "marsh gas type," H_4C; in other words, they proposed the tetravalence of carbon. The step was not considered logical at the time because the types were invented precisely for the purpose of explaining the constitution of organic compounds by analogy with simple inorganic molecules. Until the proposal of the marsh gas type, methane belonged to the $\left. \begin{array}{l} H \\ H \end{array} \right\}$ type, and methyl chloride to the $\left. \begin{array}{l} H \\ Cl \end{array} \right\}$ type, with one hydrogen atom in each type formula replaced by a methyl group. Chloroform, $CHCl_3$, had been relegated to the triple hydrochloric acid type, with one CH taking the place of three hydrogens, $\left. \begin{array}{l} CH \\ Cl_3 \end{array} \right\}$. Ironically, this formula implies the tetravalence of carbon.

The enunciation of carbon's tetravalence, however, did not immediately clarify the constitution of complex organic radicals. This clarification was published almost simultaneously in 1858 by

---

[12] H. Kolbe, *Ann.*, *101*, 257–265 (1857).
[13] Wm. Odling, *Proceedings of the Royal Institution of Great Britain*, 2, 63 (1855).
[14] F. A. Kekulé, *Ann.*, *101*, 200 (1857).

Kekulé[15] and Archibald Scott Couper[16] (1831–1892). Kekulé in a famous speech later claimed that the idea of the chain formation of carbon atoms had occurred to him at least three years earlier:

> During my stay in London I resided for a considerable time in Clapham Road in the neighborhood of Clapham Common. I frequently, however, spent my evenings with my friend Hugo Müller at Islington at the opposite end of the metropolis. We talked of many things, but most often of our beloved chemistry. One fine summer evening I was returning by the last bus, "outside," as usual, through the deserted streets of the city, which are at other times so full of life. I fell into a reverie [*Träumerei*], and lo, the atoms were gamboling before my eyes! Whenever, hitherto, these diminutive beings had appeared to me, they had always been in motion; but up to that time I had never been able to discern the nature of their motion. Now, however, I saw how, frequently, two smaller atoms united to form a pair; how a larger one embraced the two smaller ones; how still larger ones kept hold of three or even four of the smaller; whilst the whole kept whirling in a giddy dance. I saw how the larger ones formed a chain, dragging the smaller ones after them but only at the ends of the chain. I saw what our past master, Kopp, my highly honored teacher and friend, has depicted with such charm in his "Molekular-Welt"; but I saw it long before him. The cry of the conductor: "Clapham Road," awakened me from my dreaming; but I spent a part of the night in putting on paper at least sketches of these dream forms. This was the origin of the *Structural Theory*.[17]

Kekulé suggested that his early architectural studies prepared him for this contribution to structural theory. He put his ideas on paper and discussed them with his friends—but they were not encouraging. "More than a year later an article by Limpricht provided the occasion for publishing it, though of course in a modified form. The article did not gain materially from this alteration. It would have suited the purpose better had the polemical part not been printed."[17] The complete article is translated in the present volume, including the polemical part.

Couper's early training was in philosophy and classical languages. He turned to chemistry only two or three years before 1858. As seen in his papers, he approached chemical formulas unencumbered by the weight of traditional viewpoints, approaching the problem as one does a foreign language.

He gave his paper "On a New Chemical Theory" to Wurtz (in whose laboratory he was working) for presentation to the French

---

[15] F. A. Kekulé, *Ann.*, *106*, 129 (1858).

[16] A. S. Couper, *C.R. Acad. Sci.*, *46*, 1157 (1858).

[17] Part of Kekulé's speech at the Berlin Benzene Celebration; *Berichte der deutschen chemischen Gesellschaft*, *23*, 1302 (1890). Translated by F. R. Japp, *Journal of the Chemical Society*, *73*, 97 (1898); the complete translation (by the editor of this volume) appears in *J. chem. Educ.*, *35*, 21 (1958).

Academy; but Wurtz hesitated. In the meantime, Kekulé's paper was published. It is now believed that Couper's permanent breakdown in health soon afterwards was in large part attributable to this disappointment. Couper's long paper (also in this volume) appeared within a few months, giving considerable insight into the thought processes he followed.

With these papers of Kekulé and Couper, the fundamental framework of classical valence theory was in print, namely, the idea of a limited combining capacity of each kind of atom, and of the magnitude of this capacity in the case of the common elements. The theory, as will be seen in the Epilogue, did not find immediate or universal acceptance, but slowly chemists began to conform to it. The argument as to whether atoms could have more than one valence raged for many years after the valence concept had been generally accepted.

The term "valence" (*Valenz*) is believed to have been introduced into chemical discussion by C. W. Wichelhaus in 1868, while the adjectives monovalent or univalent, etc., were used by Emil Erlenmeyer and Lothar Meyer some years previously. They replaced the misleading designations of monatomic and diatomic, often used at the time.

It should be clear from the above discussion that the valence concept was not an innovation that can be credited to one man, but was rather a development almost forced upon chemists with the accumulation of chemical information. Aspects of the theory were included implicitly or explicitly in numerous papers during the 1840's and 1850's.

This collection of papers ends with the first extension of the valence concept beyond its purely numerical character. In a second example of almost simultaneous publication Jacobus Henricus van't Hoff (1852–1911) and Joseph Achille le Bel (1847–1930) developed the relation between optical activity and chemical constitution, a relation not understandable unless valence bonds had directional characteristics in space. Though le Bel framed his hypothesis in more general geometrical terms, both arrived at the proposal that the valence bonds at a carbon atom must be directed to the corners of a tetrahedron.[18, 19] Only in this way can the correct number of isomers be explained for substitution products of methane with the formulas Ca_3b, Ca_2bc, $Cabcd$, where a, b, c, d

[18] J. H. van't Hoff, *Archives Néerlandaises des Sciences Exactes et Naturelles*, 9, 445–454 (1874).

[19] J. A. le Bel, *Bulletin de la Société chimique de France*, 22, 337–347 (1874).

are different atoms or groups.   Only in the last case has more than one isomer ever been discovered.

The conception of a tetrahedral arrangement of atoms has an interesting history.   As early as 1808, William Hyde Wollaston[20] (1766–1828) had stated his view that chemists would one day have to think of atomic arrangements in three dimensions.   He further declared that when four atoms are attached to another atom, a suitable arrangement is that of a tetrahedron.   In general, however, an operational skepticism prevailed as to the possibility of determining the relative positions of atoms in space, a skepticism which reached its peak in Kolbe's scathing attack on van't Hoff.[21]   The tetrahedron is mentioned by Louis Pasteur (1822–1895) in summarizing his researches on molecular asymmetry: "Are the atoms [of dextrorotatory tartaric acid] grouped according to the spire of a dextrorse helix, or placed at the summits of an irregular tetrahedron ...?   We are unable to reply to these questions.   But what cannot be doubted is that there is a grouping of atoms according to an order dissymmetric to a non-superposable image."[22]

The first proposal that the valences of *carbon* were arranged tetrahedrally was made by Aleksandr Mikhailovich Butlerov (1828–1886) in 1862.[23]   In an attempt to explain the isomerism (now known to be illusory) of $C_2H_5.H$ and $CH_3.CH_3$, he proposed as a model a tetrahedral carbon atom, each face of which was capable of attaching a univalent atom or group.   He proceeded to calculate the number of isomers to be expected in the case of methane and its substitution products if two, three, or four of the valences of carbon (even if all bonded to hydrogen) were different in character. By assuming differences in carbon affinities he was able to explain the isomerism between "methyl" and "ethyl hydride" mentioned above.

Five years later Kekulé described a tetrahedral carbon model[24] in order to visualize the links in acetylene H—C≡C—H and hydrogen cyanide H—C≡N.   Some annotations made by Kekulé

[20] W. H. Wollaston, *Phil. Trans.*, *98*, 96–102 (1808); reprinted in *Foundations of the Atomic Theory* (Alembic Club Reprint No. 2; Chicago, University of Chicago Press, 1902), p. 34.

[21] H. Kolbe, *Journal für praktische Chemie*, [2], *15*, 473 (1877); translated in G. W. Wheland, *Advanced Organic Chemistry*, 2nd ed., New York, John Wiley & Sons, 1949, p. 132.

[22] L. Pasteur, *Leçons de chimie professées en 1860*, Chemical Society of Paris, 1861; translated in the *American Journal of Pharmacy*, *34*, 15 (1862).

[23] A. M. Butlerov, *Zeitschrift für Chemie und Pharmazie*, *5*, 297–304 (1862).

[24] F. A. Kekulé, *Zeitschrift für Chemie*, *3*, 217 (1867).

on Butlerov's earlier article have recently come to light,[25] indicating the probable path of the tetrahedron concept. Van't Hoff worked with Kekulé in 1872 and published his views two years later. Both van't Hoff and le Bel were in Wurtz's laboratory in 1873, but they do not seem to have discussed the question. Van't Hoff built his argument on the statement by Johannes Adolf Wislicenus (1835–1902)[26] that the explanation for the optical activity of the lactic acids must be sought in the spatial relations of the constituent atoms; while le Bel followed a more abstract line of reasoning regarding symmetry properties, as Pasteur had done before him.

The papers that follow aided in the construction of a remarkable symbolic language, permitting not only the association of a different symbol (a structural formula) with almost every distinct chemical substance, but also, from the details of the formula, a prediction as to the likely chemical and physical behavior of the substance. The formulas of Kekulé, Couper, van't Hoff and le Bel *worked*; they turned out to be eminently useful. Why they worked, what held atoms together and oriented valence bonds in space, remained a mystery whose unravelling took more than fifty years. The developments of that later period are surveyed in the Epilogue.

O. Theodor Benfey
Richmond, Indiana   *Department of Chemistry*
August, 1962   *Earlham College*

[25] See J. Gillis, *Mededelingen van de koninklijke Vlaamse Academie voor Wetenschappen*, **20**, 3 (1958).

[26] J. A. Wislicenus, *Ber.*, **2**, 620 (1869).

1

Friedrich Wöhler and Justus Liebig

Researches Respecting the Radical of Benzoic Acid

[From *The American Journal of Science and Arts*, 26, 261–285 (1834), slightly edited; translation by James C. Booth of "Untersuchungen über das Radikal der Benzoesäure," *Annalen der Pharmacie*, 3, 249–287 (1832), reprinted under the same title by the Akademische Verlagsgesellschaft, Leipzig, 1891, as Ostwald's *Klassiker der exakten Wissenschaften* No. 22, edited by H. Kopp.]

When in the dark province of organic nature, we succeed in finding a light point, appearing to be one of those inlets whereby we may attain to the examination and investigation of this province, then we have reason to congratulate ourselves, although conscious that the object before us is unexhausted. In such an area, where previous researches and materials are of so little help, comprehensive and detailed studies cannot as yet be expected. With such a view, let us examine the following experiments; which, as it regards their extent and connection, present a wide field for cultivation.

The substance with which we commence our undertaking, is the fluid oil of bitter almonds, distinguished from other similar bodies, by the property, first rightly investigated by Stange, of being converted in the air, by the absorption of oxygen, into an acid, into the benzoic acid, and which appeared to lay claim to the highest interest from the manner in which it arises from bodies apparently so different. Another peculiarity, which long since drew the attention of chemists and pharmaceutists to the oil, is its containing prussic acid, whose presence seems to bear fixed relations to the nature of the oil. Among the many researches to which these properties have given rise, we mention only the latest by Robiquet and Boutron-Charlard.[1] As one of the facts most worthy of remark, they observe in their essay, that the fluid oil of bitter almonds, as a whole has its constituents in the almonds and appears to proceed from these constituents first by the action of water. For by the use of alcohol, it disappears altogether and can then in general be no more produced from the almonds; but in place of it they obtained a crystallizable

---

[1] Annales de Chimie et de Physique, Vol. xliv, 352.

body, the amygdalin, formerly unknown to exist and which appeared to them to be the only cause of the peculiar bitter taste of the almonds, and one of the compound elements of the fluid bitter almond oil.[2]

We have been obliged to leave out of the limit of the present essay, the consideration of the question, whether this oil exists ready formed in the almond, or is generated in the course of the producing process from the fixed constituents,—and a closer examination of amygdalin and its connection with the supposed generation of the oil. The clearing up of this point must be made the subject of particular experiments. To fix firmly the station from which the inquiry took its rise, we make the general remark beforehand, that in consequence of our experiments, we believe that there is a body composed of three elements, always remaining the same in its behavior towards other agents, and which can be considered not alone as the radical of benzoic acid, but at the same time as the root perhaps with slight variations of a multitude of similar combinations. But here we venture to assert, that it would be improper to look for this in the camphorid,[3] whose very existence appears to us questionable, although it is placed here by Dumas without a single demonstrative experiment. A series of phenomena intimately connected with each other was the only guide which presented itself to our view. Suffer us to say that to a certainty we believe a multitude of similar radicals will readily be discovered by calculation and spontaneous changes in the analyses of organic substances, which chemists have undertaken; but here we stop, for science is but little profited by the raising of expectations, as yet unsupported by facts.

Bitter Almond Oil. The crude oil, which served as the material for our experiments possesses a faint yellow color, the well known peculiar odor and proved itself in all its reactions, and other relations to be a decidedly pure product. We are indebted for it to the kindness of Mr. Pelouze.

---

[2] In the same essay, Messrs. Robiquet and Boutron-Charlard, express their conviction of the preexistence of benzoic in hippuric acid; now the chief reason on which they rely is an evident error in the Annales de Chimie, V. 43, p. 197, thus instead of saying "Si l'on cesse de chauffer au moment même qu'on sent les vapeurs sulphureuses qu'on mêle la masse noire avec de l'eau et qu'on la fasse bouillïr avec de la chaux, l'acide hydrochlorique en separe ensuite de l'acide benzoique," it should read, "n'en separe point ensuite de l'acide benzoique."

The conclusion as drawn from the unrectified phrase, is in itself contradictory; and this caused the correctness of the sentence to be questioned, which the German copy would have confirmed.

[3] [Camphorid is the name Dumas in 1831 gave to a hydrocarbon which he assumed to be present in oil of turpentine and camphor (Kopp, *op. cit.*, p. 38). —O.T.B.]

FRIEDRICH WÖHLER (1800–1882). After a drawing by J. Ehrentraut. From *Das Buch der Grossen Chemiker* (Dr. Günther Bugge, editor), Vol. II. Berlin, 1930. Courtesy of the publisher, Verlag Chemie, Weinheim/Bergstr.

JUSTUS LIEBIG (1803–1873). From *The Illustrated London News*, May 3, 1873.

Treated with alkali, acid, or a salt of iron, this oil contains a considerable quantity of prussic acid, and apart from the air, either by itself or with potassa, readily changes into benzoic acid.

We were soon convinced that the content of prussic acid bears no relation to the formation of benzoic acid, and endeavored therefore to obtain a pure oil, free from the benzoic and prussic acids and from water. This purpose was fully accomplished in the following manner.

The crude oil was carefully mixed with hydrate of potassa and a solution of chloride of iron by strong agitation and then submitted to distillation. The whole of the oil passed over with the water, and perfectly free from prussic acid. By means of a tube, it was separated from the water, and redistilled in a dry apparatus over freshly burned, powdered chalk.

The oil obtained in this manner is pure, free from benzoic and prussic acids and water, perfectly colorless, very fluid, and has a strong refractive power; its odor is but little different from that of the crude oil; its taste is burning aromatic. It is heavier than water, its sp. gr. 1.043. Its boiling point is so high that we could not determine it with our thermometers, which extended not above 130° centigrade.[4] It is easily inflammable, burning with a bright sooty flame.

Urged through a red-hot glass tube, it remains undecomposed. In the air, in moist or dry oxygen, it is entirely converted in crystallized benzoic acid. In the sun's ray this change is remarkably hastened, beginning in the course of a few moments. The same change takes place in the air by the presence of water and potassa, with the formation of benzoate of potassa. If these experiments be made in a glass tube closed with mercury, the rise of this metal proves the absorption of oxygen.

Beside this conversion of the oil into benzoic acid, no third body is formed.

The manner of its purification shews that it is not decomposed or changed by anhydrous alkali, but to the hydrated, its behavior is different. Heated with the hydrate of potassa, apart from the air, it forms benzoate of potassa and evolves pure hydrogen gas.

If the oil be introduced into solution of hydrate of potassa in water, or into alcohol saturated with ammoniacal gas, it is immediately dissolved, and if the air be wholly excluded, a benzoate appears which when potassa is employed, is soon deposited in large shining lamellar crystals. By the addition of water which dissolves

---

[4] When temperature is mentioned in this essay, the degrees will be understood to refer to the centigrade thermometer.—J.B.

the salt, an oily body is separated, which is no longer the oil of bitter almonds.[5]

In the concentrated nitric and sulphuric acids, the pure bitter almond oil is soluble without change. By heating the latter solution, it first becomes a purple-red, and then black with the evolution of sulphurous acid.

From the action of chlorine and bromine, new compounds arise which will be described in another part of this essay.

The composition of this pure oil was ascertained in the usual way by ignition with the oxide of copper. To expel the hygroscopic moisture from the oxide of copper, we have employed in our experiments a small air pump invented by Gay-Lussac. Since it has not been described by himself, we take the liberty of annexing a sketch of the same; for it may undoubtedly be viewed as one of the most important improvements with which organic analysis has been enriched, both as regards its convenience in use and the safety it ensures in hydrogen examinations.

Fig. 1. is the pump alone of half the actual size; it is furnished with common bladder valves, and terminates beneath in a strong screw, to fasten it firmly for use.

Fig. 2. shews the pump as connected with the ignition tube *a*, which is united by means of a well fitting cork with a long tube *b*, filled with chloride of calcium. *c*, Fig. 2. is a glass tube about thirty inches in length fastened above to the pump by a short and broad piece of a tube, and dipping below in mercury. It has no other object than to prove by the rise of the mercury that all the connections of cork and caoutchouc are tightly closed, and it is removed as soon as the pump is put in operation. Indeed it may be dispensed with altogether, since the tightness may be judged of after a little practice, by the force with which the air rushes in through the opened cock *d*, after exhaustion.

To the table is screwed a strong wooden post *e*, Fig. 2. on which the pump is fastened by its screw. The moisture contained in the oxide of copper mixture is expelled at the same time, with the air by exhausting the ignition tube, from which by degrees the last trace is removed, since the air dried by the chloride of calcium is often admitted by repeated exhaustions and opening of the stop-cock.

It is evident that the expulsion of moisture may be hastened,

---

[5] [The new oil is benzyl alcohol, $C_6H_5CH_2OH$. It is produced together with a salt of benzoic acid, $C_6H_5CO_2H$, when benzaldehyde or oil of bitter almonds, C_6H_5CHO, is treated with a base. The reaction has become known as the Cannizzaro reaction (1853).—O.T.B.]

from substances from which we have to fear no loss by warmth, if the ignition tube be put into a tin tube filled with hot water.[6]

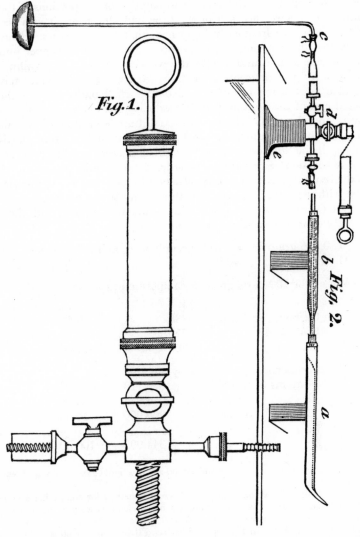

[6] This pump may be used with great convenience for drying substances which suffer drying only in a vacuum, at the common or a slightly raised temperature. In place of the ignition tube, a short tube is fastened on which is closed beneath, or a small glass globe, in which is placed the substance to be dried.

This small air pump presents yet another advantage, of which we frequently availed ourselves in our experiments. The oil and other fluids submitted by us to analysis possess so high a boiling point, that the small bulb filled with them, was emptied of the portions of the liquid, not before this part of the tube had almost attained a red heat. It thence frequently happened, that the gas was suddenly evolved with such violence, as to throw some oxide of copper into the chloride of lime, and thereby the experiment became unavailing, at least for the determination of hydrogen. This is completely avoided by turning the open end of the small bulbs towards the closed end of the ignition tube, introducing the oxide of copper in layers and then exhausting. The small bubble of atmospheric air in the bulbs, now suffices to expel all the contained moisture, particularly if the ignition tube be brought to a more vertical position, and exhaustion be repeated. In order not to mention the accuracy of the result disadvantageously, it may be added that this manipulation with very fluid substances is throughout superfluous.

We return to the pure oil of bitter almonds. Ignited with these precautionary measures, it yielded,

I. 0.386 gramme[7] = 1.109 carbonic acid, and 0.200 water.
II. 0.341   ,,   = 0.982   ,,   ,,   ,, 0.175 ,,

Which for 100 parts gives its composition as

	I.		II.
Carbon, . . .	79.438	. . .	79.603
Hydrogen, . .	5.756	. . .	5.734
Oxygen, . . .	14.808	. . .	14.663

These proportions calculated by volume[8] give

14 atoms of carbon, .	1070.118	.	79.56
12 ,, hydrogen,[9] .	74.877	.	5.56
2 ,, oxygen, .	200.000	.	14.88
	1344.995		100.00

[7] The gramme is always to be understood as the weight or series of weights employed.—J.B.

[8] ["Calculated by volume" refers to Berzelius' method for computing atomic weights. He assumed that the atomic weights of elements were proportional to their densities in the gaseous state. Whereas Berzelius used an atomic weight scale based on $O = 100$, Liebig and Wöhler based their atomic weights on $O = 10$. Their other atomic weights, to four significant figures, are: $H = 0.6240$, $C = 7.644$, $N = 8.852$, $Cl = 22.13$, $Ag = 135.2$ (cf. Kopp, *op. cit.*, p. 39).—O.T.B.]

[9] [The number of atoms correspond to twice those used at present. $C_7H_6O = C_6H_5CHO$.—O.T.B.]

According to the composition of this body, the formation of benzoic acid by the mere reception of oxygen is wholly inexplicable, because in this change no other products could be detected. According to the analysis of benzoic acid by Berzelius, it contains 15 atoms of carbon, 12 of hydrogen and 3 of oxygen. This circumstance induced us to repeat the analysis of the crystallized acid, and of the same united to a base.

Analysis of Benzoic Acid. We employed for this analysis not only the common benzoic acid obtained from resin, but also a portion prepared expressly for this purpose from the oil. In both cases, we assured ourselves of their purity. The acid was fused, weighed and introduced by pieces into the ignition tube; this was then warmed to the fusion of the acid, and equally parted at half the length of the tube upon the sides. It was then filled with warm oxide of copper, again brought before the air-pump, and submitted to ignition, which with this very volatile substance could be but slowly conducted.

				Carbon.		Water.
I. 0.523 gramme of acid yielded				1.308	. .	0.238
II. 0.522	,,	,,	,,	1.302	. .	——
III. 0.305	,,	,,	,,	0.760	. .	0.136.

According to these results then, the analyses gave for 100 parts,

	I.	II.	III.
Carbon, . . .	69.155	. 68.970 . .	68.902
Hydrogen, . .	5.050	. Water was lost.	5.000
Oxygen, . . .	25.795	. . . . .	26.098

These numbers give the atomic composition of the same, as

14 atoms carbon, . . .	107.0118	69.25
12 ,, hydrogen, . .	7.4877	4.86
4 ,, oxygen, . .	40.0000	25.89
	154.4995	100.00

The variation of the composition of benzoic acid, thus obtained, from that which Berzelius found by the analysis of the benzoate of lead, caused us at first to mistrust our own analysis. Upon nearer inspection however, we found it necessary to admit, that the cause of the difference between the two analyses should be sought in the composition of the salt analyzed by Berzelius. We therefore undertook the analysis of the acid united to a base, and chose the benzoate of silver because of the facility with which it is obtained pure and crystallized, and because the oxide of silver shews but little disposition to form compounds.

Neutral nitrate of silver mixed with an alkaline benzoate in solution, gave a thick white precipitate, which by warmth became crystalline, and completely dissolved in a greater quantity of boiling water. By cooling the solution, oxide of silver was deposited in long shining crystals, which by drying under the air pump, neither lost their lustre, nor diminished in weight.

By heating in a porcelain crucible, this salt melts, puffs up, and after the deposited charcoal is consumed, leaves very white metallic silver. In this manner we determined the atomic weight of the acid.

I. 0.391 gramme of benzoate of silver left 0.184 of metallic silver.
II. 0.436   ,,   of the same gave   0.205.

According to these numbers, the composition of the salt is,

	I.	II.
Oxide of silver,	50.56	50.52
Benzoic acid,	49.44	49.48

And the atomic weight of the acid as the mean of both analyses, is 142.039.

We now submitted the salt of silver to ignition with oxide of copper, and obtained from 0.600 grammes of the salt, 0.797 grammes of carbonic acid, and 0.122 of water.

The composition of the acid, as deduced from these numbers, consists in 100 parts of

Carbon,	74.378
Hydrogen,	4.567
Oxygen,	21.055

Calculating from the atomic weight already found, we obtain,

14 atoms carbon,[10]	107.0118	74.43
10 ,, hydrogen,	6.2397	4.34
3 ,, oxygen,	30.0000	21.23
	143.2515	100.00

By comparing the analysis of the crystallized acid with that combined with the oxide of silver, it is at once evident that the difference between them is that the former contains one atom of water, which is wanting in the latter.

The only difference then between the analysis of Berzelius[11] and our own, lies in this content of water. For from the atomic weight

---

[10] [The formula is that of benzoic anhydride $(C_6H_5CO)_2O$. The formulas of acids were often represented in the anhydrous form as the water was not considered significant.—O.T.B.]

[11] [In the letter attached at the end of this article Berzelius comments on these analyses.—O.T.B.]

found by Berzelius, as well as from the behavior of the oxide of lead, it follows that the oxide by union with benzoic acid, does not separate the water of the same, but that this water enters into the composition of the salt.   On being heated, and especially in the crystallized state, when, as we have just seen, it contains one atom of water, it loses a portion of its acidity.

In fact, if from the atomic weight of benzoic acid, as obtained by

Berzelius from the oxide of lead, namely, .   .   .   152.1423
We take off one atom of water, ...   11.2479

We get for the atomic weight of the dry acid, .   140.8944.

If according to this corrected atomic weight, we calculate the carbon and hydrogen of Berzelius' analysis, we likewise obtain 14 atoms of carbon and 10 of hydrogen.

These comparisons will suffice to remove every doubt respecting the composition of benzoic acid and the statement of Dumas,[11a] that this acid contains hydrogen and oxygen in the same proportion as water, is certainly an error, which he will undoubtedly correct.

Returning from this digression to the consideration of the oil of bitter almonds, and its conversion into crystallized benzoic acid, we now find this phenomenon capable of an easy explanation.   The acid is formed by simple oxydation, the oil absorbing in the air or in oxygen gas, 2 atoms of this element.

The formation of benzoate of potassa from the oil, when the latter is heated with hydrate of potassa, depends upon the decomposition of the water in the hydrate, whereby the oil takes one atom of oxygen, while hydrogen escapes in the form of gas.

We have farther mentioned that the oil with a solution of potassa in alcohol, forms likewise without the access of air a benzoate of potassa, and that then by the addition of water, an oily body separates from the alcohol possessed of different properties.   As far as we have examined this new body, it admits of no doubt, that in case the constituents of alcohol do not enter into its composition, it originates either from taking oxygen from the bitter almond oil, or from the decomposition of water.   In the former case it would be composed according to the formula $C^{14}H^{12}O$, in the latter the formula $C^{14}H^{14}O^2$.[12]

After the determining of this point, and a reviewing of the combining relations of bitter almond oil yet to be considered, we believe

---

[11a] *Ann. chim. phys.*, 47, 202.
[12] [The second guess was better. Actually even more hydrogen is absorbed: $2C_6H_5CH_2OH = C_{14}H_{16}O_2$.—O.T.B.]

it naturally follows that this oil is in its pure state a hydrogen compound, wherein the radical of benzoic acid is combined with 2 atoms of hydrogen, instead of with oxygen as in the acid. This radical as yet unobtained insulated, is composed of $C^{14}H^{10}O^2$. We call it *benzöyl*, (the ending from ὕλη material, matter.) The consequent name for the pure oil of bitter almonds is *hydrobenzöyl* (hydroguret of benzöyl,) and for the benzoic acid, *benzöylic acid*, (benzöyl acid). We will however use the common names benzoic acid and bitter almond oil, except in theoretical demonstrations. We will see how easily the remaining relations, to which we now come, will be perceived and comprehended.

Chlorobenzöyl. If through the bitter almond oil (hydrobenzöyl) we conduct dry chlorine gas, the latter is absorbed with considerable heat, and hydrochloric acid is evolved; but besides this, no other product which warrants the conclusion of a farther decomposition. As soon as the formation of hydrochloric acid begins to cease, the liquid becomes yellow from the solution of chlorine, but the overcharge of this gas is again expelled by boiling. Finally, if the liquid, be heated to boiling, in contact with chlorine, and the formation of hydrochloric acid is no longer perceived, we obtain a new compound, perfectly pure. This is the chlorobenzöyl, (chloride of benzöyl).

The chlorobenzöyl is a transparent fluid of the sp. gr. 1.196. It possesses a peculiar odor in the highest degree penetrating; in particular, strongly affecting the eyes, and reminding us of the pungent odor of horse-radish. Its boiling point is very high: it is inflammable, burning with a bright, green-edged, sooty flame.

It sinks in water as an oil, without solution. After a considerable time, or sooner by boiling, it separates entirely into crystallized benzoic acid and hydro-chloric acid. It suffers the same change if kept in moist air for a length of time. If chlorine be conducted through a mixture of hydrobenzöyl and water, the oil disappears, and the water congeals into a crystalline mass of benzoic acid.

The chloride of benzöyl may be distilled unchanged over anhydrated baryta and lime.

Warmed with alkalies and water, this chloride forms at the same time a chloride of the metal and a benzoate of the alkali.

In all these decompositions beside the benzoic and hydro-chloric acids, no third body is formed, whence it clearly follows, that in this compound, chlorine and benzöyl must be in such proportion, that by the separation of water into its constituents, these last, exactly suffice to form on the one side hydrochloric, and on the other anhydrated benzoic acid,—the latter, at the moment of its formation, taking up one atom of water.   Hydrobenzöyl (bitter almond oil) consists of,

$$(14C + 10H + 2O) + 2H.$$

By the action of chlorine, two atoms of hydrogen unite with two atoms of chlorine to form hydro-chloric acid, which is evolved.   But the hydrogen gives place to two atoms of chlorine according to the following formula;

$$(14C + 10H + 2O) + 2Cl.$$

With the constituents of water this body is decomposed in such a manner that two atoms of hydrogen unite with two atoms of chlorine to form hydrochloric acid, while the freed oxygen unites with benzöyl and forms benzoic acid.

By analysis we proved the correctness of the composition.   We dissolved it in dilute ammonia, super-saturated it with nitric-acid and precipitated by the nitrate of silver.   0.719 grm. Chlorobenzöyl gave 0.712 gm. chloride of silver.   This gives for 100 pts. 24.423 of chlorine.

Ignition with oxide of copper in the common way, where the fluid in small bulbs is placed in the ignition tube, proved altogether impracticable and indeed upon the grounds already mentioned. All these experiments failed us, since every time, even by the most cautious heating, the content of the small bulb, or the fluid present in the oxide of copper, was at once converted into gas, and thereby either the oxide was thrown into the chloride of calcium, or a part of the substance was carried away unignited.

It was therefore necessary to introduce the weighed fluid by drops among the *oxide* of copper; by a slow progressive heating we succeeded perfectly in terminating the ignition without difficulty.

0.534 gm. Chlorobenzöyl yield 1.188 carbonic acid and 1.180 of water, which in 100 pts. gives,

Carbon,	60.83
Hydrogen,	3.74
Oxygen,	11.01
Chlorine,	24.42

From these numbers we obtain by volume as the theoretical result,

14 atoms of	Carbon,	107.018		60.02
10 „	Hydrogen,	6.239		3.51
2 „	Oxygen,	20.000		11.55
2 „	Chlorine,	44.265		24.92
		177.522		100.00

By calculation the numbers yield a somewhat smaller quantity of carbon and hydrogen than was obtained by analysis. The reason undoubtedly is that in preparing the chlorine compound, perhaps $\frac{1}{1000}$ of the *oil of bit. alm.* escapes with the chlorine. In no case is the difference of such importance, that the conclusion to which we arrive respecting the composition of this body, can be considered false.

With respect to the properties of chlorobenzöyl we have yet to remark that by warmth it dissolves phosphorus and sulphur, which by cooling again separate in the crystalline form. With sulphuret of carbon, it may be mingled in every proportion, and, as it would seem, without suffering decomposition. With solid chloride of phosphorus, it becomes strongly heated, with the formation of liquid chloride of phosphorus and an oily, strongly smelling body which we have not farther examined.

The very remarkable behavior of chlorobenzöyl in dry ammoniacal gas, and its decomposition with alcohol, we will treat of in a separate part of this essay.

If chlorobenzöyl be treated with metallic bromides, iodides, sulphurets or cyanurets, such an exchange of constituents ensues, that a metallic chloride on the one hand, and a combination of benzöyl with bromine, iodine, sulphur or cyanogen on the other hand, are generated, which are composed similarly to the chlorobenzöyl.

Bromobenzöyl. This compound is formed directly by mixing bromine with hydrobenzöyl (bitter almond oil). The mixture becomes heated and throws forth thick vapors of hydrobromic acid. By heating still farther, this acid as well as the excess of bromine is expelled.

The bromobenzöyl (bromide of benzöyl) is a large foliated, crystalline mass of a brownish color, soft and at common temperature nearly semifluid. It melts by a gentle warmth into a brownish yellow fluid. It possesses an analogous odor to the chloride, though much fainter and therefore aromatic. In the air it smokes faintly, but fumes strongly upon a slight elevation of temperature. It is combustible and burns with a bright and smoky flame.

By water it is slowly decomposed. Warmed under the same, it becomes a brownish oil, and after long boiling separates into the hydrobromic and crystallized benzoic acids.

In alcohol and ether it is readily soluble without decomposition. By dilution it may be obtained from both in a crystalline form.

Iodobenzöyl. This compound seems not to be formed by the direct union of its constituents. It may however readily be formed by warming iodide of potassa with chloride of benzöyl. It may be distilled over as a brown fluid, which congeals to a brown crystalline mass. It then contains iodine dissolved. In its pure state it is a colorless, foliated, crystalline substance, easily fusible, but by this operation is always decomposed with the formation of some iodine. In odor, behavior to water and alcohol, and in inflammability, it does not differ from the preceding compound.

Sulphuret of Benzöyl. This may be obtained by distilling the chloride with sulphuret of lead. It passes over as a yellow oil, which congeals to a yellow, soft and crystalline mass. It possesses a disagreeable odor resembling sulphur. It seems not to be decomposed by boiling with water. With a boiling solution of caustic potassa, it slowly forms benzoate of potassa and sulphuret of potassium. With alcohol it is not decomposed. It is inflammable and burns with a bright, sooty flame, evolving sulphurous acid.

Cyanobenzöyl. Hydrobenzöyl dissolves a certain quantity of cyanogen and receives also its odor, but by warming this gas may be again expelled without change.

The true compound we obtained by distilling chlorobenzöyl over cyanuret of mercury. The compound passes over as a gold colored oil, and mercury remains behind.

In its pure, fresh state, the cyanobenzöyl, (cyanuret of benzöyl) is a colorless fluid, but it rapidly changes to yellow. It possesses a pungent odor, strongly exciting tears, and at a distance resembles oil of cinnamon. Its taste is biting, sweetish, and afterward much like prussic acid.

It is heavier than water, in which it sinks as an oil, and by which it is soon converted into benzoic and hydrocyanic acids. If a drop be suffered to spread upon water, it will be found completely changed in a day into a radiating mass of benzoic acid crystals. By boiling with water, it is rapidly decomposed into the benzoic and prussic acids. It is readily inflammable, burning with a white, but very smoky flame.

Benzamide. By conducting dry ammonia over pure chlorobenzöyl, the former is absorbed with much heat, and the liquid is converted into a white, solid mass, consisting of a mixture of muriate of ammonia[13] and a new body which we call *Benzamide*. For in its behavior and composition it bears a perfect analogy to oxamide.

The perfect saturation of chlorobenzöyl with ammonia takes place at first with such violence, that it is slowly and difficultly attained; for the rising solid mass soon begins to protect the yet unsaturated portion from farther contact of the gas. It is therefore

---

[13] [Muriate of ammonia is ammonium chloride.—O.T.B.]

often necessary to take the mass out of the vessel, crush it and again continue the action of ammonia.

It may be inferred from the formation of muriate of ammonia at the same time, that by the union of the two bodies, a decomposition of ammonia takes place; for, as we have before remarked, the chlorine in chlorobenzöyl is contained as chlorine and not as hydrochloric acid.

It is indeed imaginable that the exchange of elements happens when water is poured over the white mass to expel the muriate of ammonia; but the behavior of cyanobenzöyl sufficiently proves, that this separation first occurs, the moment the ammoniacal gas comes in contact with the chlorobenzöyl.

The cyanobenzöyl suffers an altogether analogous change in ammonia to the chlorine compound; it forms benzamide and cyanuret of ammonia, which latter rises in consequence of its fluidity, with the excess of ammonia, and sublimes in the form of brilliant crystals.

To isolate benzamide, the muriate of ammonia formed is washed out of the white mass with cold water, and the remaining benzamide is dissolved in boiling water. By cooling, the solution deposits crystals.

By neglecting perfectly to dry the ammonia over burnt lime or hydrate of potassa, a corresponding mass of benzoate of ammonia is formed, by the action of the moist gas upon the chlorobenzöyl, and the same proportion of the new body is lost.

Also when the chlorobenzöyl has not been fully saturated with ammonia, then upon treating the mass with hot water, the formed benzamide, as is proved by its behavior to acids, is either wholly or in part decomposed according to the quantity of free chlorobenzöyl.

Lastly under certain circumstances, (of which we yet know but little, but it is probable chiefly when the chlorobenzöyl was not perfectly free from chlorine), by saturation with ammonia an oily body may be observed, possessing an aromatic odor resembling bitter almonds, and by which the contained benzamide has the property, before it is dissolved, to melt to an oil by warming with water, and again to separate from the solution in the form of drops of oil, which congeal in a short time.

Pure benzamide shews a remarkable phenomenon in its crystallization. It deposites from a boiling hot solution by rapid cooling, pearly, leafy crystals very similar to chlorate of potassa. By long cooling and at a certain concentration, the whole liquid congeals to a white mass consisting of very fine, silky crystals resembling caffein. After one or more days and often after a few hours, large cavities may be observed in this mass, in the centre of which may be observed one single or several large well formed crystals, into which the silky fibre has been converted; and gradually this change of form spreads throughout the mass.

The form of the crystals of benzamide is a right-rhombic prism, which by the enlarging of two opposite planes becomes tabular.[13a] They have a highly nacreous lustre, are transparent and exhibit upon water a fattiness, easily swimming on its surface.

At 115° C. it melts to a water-like liquid, which congeals by cooling to a large-leaved crystalline mass, wherein are frequently found cavities with well formed crystals. At a stronger heat it boils and distills over unchanged. Its vapor is similar in odor to bitter almond oil. It is easily inflammable and burns with a sooty flame.

In cold water, the crystallized benzamide is so little soluble that the solution scarcely possesses taste. In alcohol on the contrary it is readily soluble. In boiling ether it is also dissolved, and from this solution in particular can be obtained in well defined crystals.

Covered with caustic potassa at common temperature, the benzamide evolves no ammonia. Nor does its solution mingled with a salt of iron at common temperature give a precipitate, as indeed it in general gives no reaction with a metallic salt. By boiling the benzamide with a concentrated solution of caustic potassa, ammonia is evolved in abundance and a benzoate of potassa remains. By heating to boiling the solution of benzamide mixed with a salt of iron, it becomes cloudy and throws down a benzoate of iron.

By dissolving benzamide in a strong acid with boiling, it disappears, and in its place benzoic acid in crystals separates from the cooled solution, while an ammoniacal salt has formed. By employing hot concentrated sulphuric acid, the formed benzoic acid sublimes. If boiled with pure water, even for a considerable length of time, this change into benzoic acid and ammonia does not take place.

The analysis of benzamide is easily effected by ignition with oxide of copper. The relative proportion of nitrogen and carbon was ascertained by the ignition of the substance "*in vacuo.*" The ignition tube was provided at one end with a thirty inch tube, the one end dipping in mercury, and the other drawn out to a strong point, which by means of a caoutchouc tube could be connected with the small air-pump.

The air was then exhausted, and as soon as the mercury had risen in the tube to the height of some twenty seven inches, the point at the other end of the ignition tube was closed by the blowpipe, and the ignition was commenced.

From these experiments it followed that nitrogen and carbon

[13a] [Booth's translation here abbreviates a complex crystallographic description in the original.—O.T.B.]

were evolved in the proportion of one to fourteen. It yielded farther,

		Carbonic acid.	Water.
I.	0.400 grm. benzamide	$=1.012$ . . .	$+0.208$
II.	0.489 ,, ,,	$=1.235$ . . .	$+0.253$

Calculated from these, benzamide contains in one hundred parts,

		I.	II.
Carbon,	. . . . .	69.954	69.816
Hydrogen,	. . . .	5.780	5.790
Nitrogen,	. . . . .	11.563	11.562
Oxygen,	. . . . .	12.603	12.832

By volume these numbers give as the theoretical result,

14 atoms	Carbon,	. . .	107.0118 . . .	69.73
14 ,,	Hydrogen,	. . .	8.7360 . . .	5.69
2 ,,	Nitrogen,	. . .	17.7036 . . .	11.53
2 ,,	Oxygen,	. . .	20.0000 . . .	13.05
			153.4514	100.00

This composition clearly explains not merely the manner of the formation of benzamide, but also its behavior with acids and potassa, that is, its conversion into benzoic acid and ammonia.

If 2 atoms[13b] of ammonia be added to the composition of chloride of benzöyl, we obtain the formula;

$$\begin{aligned} 14C + 10H + 2O + 2Cl &= \text{chlorobenzöyl} \\ 12H \qquad\qquad\quad +4N &= \text{ammonia} \\ \hline 14C + 22H + 2O + 2Cl + 4N. \end{aligned}$$

Abstract from this 2 atoms muriate of ammonia,

$$\begin{aligned} 14C + 22H + 2O + 2Cl + 4N \\ 8H \qquad +2Cl + 2N, \text{ we then obtain} \\ \hline 14C + 14H + 2O + \qquad 2N, \end{aligned}$$

which is the true composition of benzamide and by adding to this last 1 atom of water, the formula becomes, $14C + 16H + 3O + 2N$ which expresses the true composition of neutral dry benzoate of ammonia. This salt consists of

$$\begin{aligned} 1 \text{ atom benzoic acid,} &= 14C + 10H + 3O \\ 1 \quad ,, \quad \text{ammonia} &= \qquad 6H \qquad + 2N \\ \hline 14C + 16H + 3O + 2N. \end{aligned}$$

Benzamide exhibits some phenomena in its decomposition which deserve an ampler consideration than we have bestowed upon them.

[13b] [For "2 atoms" the original erroneously read "4 atoms."—O.T.B.]

Heated with a larger quantity of dry caustic baryta, it partially fuses, appears to become a hydrate, evolves ammonia, and then distills over a colorless, oily body, deserving notice.[14] It is lighter than water, in which it is insoluble. It possesses an aromatic, sweetish taste not unlike that of fluid chloride of carbon (C^2Cl^5) and discovers itself particularly by its almost sugar-sweet taste.[15] This oil burns with a clear flame, and is changed neither by caustic alkali nor by acids; even potassium may be melted in it by gentle warmth without change.

The same substance is evolved in considerable quantity and unaccompanied by ammonia, when benzamide and potassium are melted together, in which case the latter without much violence appears to be almost wholly converted into cyanuret of potassium.

If the vapor of benzamide be conducted through an ignited narrow glass tube, only a small portion is decomposed and that without depositing a trace of carbon. The greatest part passes over unchanged, mingled with a small quantity of the sweet tasting oil before mentioned. This is evidently a peculiar substance, which by its behavior intimates an altogether simple composition and certainly deserves much attention.

Chlorobenzöyl and Alcohol. The chlorobenzöyl may be mingled with alcohol in every proportion. By observing the mixture, it will be remarked that it begins to grow warm in the course of a few minutes and this warmth increases to such a degree, that the fluid enters into self-ebullition, throwing off at the same time thick vapors of hydrochloric acid. If water be poured over it when the action is ended, then separates an oily body, colorless, sinking in water and possessing an aromatic, fruit-like odor. Washed with water and heated with chloride of calcium, it is freed from water, alcohol and acid, with which it may be adulterated.

We could not long remain in doubt respecting the nature of this new product; it must be benzoic ether.[16] For if the decomposition of chlorobenzöyl by alcohol be analogous to that by water, as is suggested by the formation of hydrochloric acid, then through the decomposition of water in the alcohol, must benzoic acid on the one hand be formed and ether on the other; which two at the moment of their origin unite to form benzoic ether. On account of its unexpected appearance, we sought to assure ourselves by an analysis,

---

[14] [Wöhler and Liebig had prepared benzonitrile C_6H_5CN.—O.T.B.]

[15] [The "fluid chloride of carbon" was discovered by Liebig in 1831 and given the formula C_2Cl_5. Dumas in 1834 correctly determined its composition as $CHCl_3$ and named it chloroform (Kopp, *op. cit.*, p. 40).—O.T.B.]

[16] [Benzoic ether is our ethyl benzoate, $C_6H_5CO_2C_2H_5$.—O.T.B.]

particularly as this analysis would give us great control over the composition of benzoic acid.

We did not employ the fluid for analysis, until after careful washing with water, the latter was entirely abstracted, by repeated digestion with muriate of lime, and by several distillations in a dried apparatus. It is to no purpose to distil it over chloride of calcium, because its boiling point is so high, that water passes over at the same time. 0.622 gm. gave 1.632 carbonic acid and 0.375 water, which in 100 parts is equivalent to,

Carbon, ...	72.529
Hydrogen, ...	6.690
Oxygen, ...	20.781

Or by volume,

18 atoms Carbon, ...	137.5866	. . .	72.37
20 „ Hydrogen, . . .	12.4796	. . .	6.56
4 „ Oxygen, . . .	40.0000	. . .	21.07
	190.0662		100.00

These proportions exactly point out a compound of,

		C H O
1 atom dry benzoic acid,	. . .	= 14—10—3
with one atom of ether,	. . .	= 4—10—1
		18—20—4

To assure ourselves of the perfect identity of benzoic ether thus formed, with that prepared after the common method, we produced the latter in abundance by the distillation of benzoic acid with a mixture of alcohol and hydrochloric acid. By comparing the two properties of the two bodies obtained by such different methods, not the slightest difference was observable. Odor, taste, sp. gr. and behavior to acid and alkali, were in both precisely the same.

The analysis of benzoic ether, by Dumas, varies materially from ours in the hydrogen content. Let this serve to shew how difficult it is to become free from preconceived opinions in researches of a similar kind.

Benzoin. The body which we would denote by this name on account of its relation to the substances treated of in this essay, has indeed been already examined by Stange, but scarcely farther than in its external properties. It is the same which is introduced into chemical works as camphor or camphoroid of bitter almond oil.

Benzoin arises under certain circumstances from the oil of bitter almonds. We obtained it, for example, accidentally, as others have done before us, by the rectification of the oil with caustic potassa, where it remains swimming upon the potassa. We produced it however in greater quantity by suffering the bitter almond oil, to stand several weeks with a concentrated solution of caustic potassa.[17] Robiquet and Charlard, have also noticed the same change in contact with alkali when free from the access of air. We can confirm this observation. In our experiment the oil was almost wholly converted into solid benzoin, though only after several weeks. Lastly, we produced it by saturating water with bitter almond oil and mingling the solution with some caustic potassa. In a few days the benzoin begins to deposit in needle-form crystals.

In all these cases the benzoin possesses at first more or less a yellow color, but is rendered perfectly pure and colorless by solution in hot alcohol, treatment with blood charcoal and frequent crystallization.

Benzoin forms clear, highly lustrous, prismatic crystals. It possesses neither taste nor smell. At 120° it melts to a colorless liquid, which again congeals to a large striated crystalline mass. At a stronger heat it boils and distils over unchanged. It is inflammable, and burns with a clear, sooty flame. It is insoluble in cold water, but if the latter be boiling, a small portion is dissolved, which again separates by cooling in capillary crystals. It is taken up by hot alcohol in much larger quantity than by cold.

It is decomposed neither by concentrated nitric acid, nor by a boiling solution of caustic potassa. With concentrated sulphuric acid on the contrary, it at first gives a violet blue solution soon becoming brown and by warming it takes a deep green color with the evolution of sulphuric acid and blackening of the whole mass.

This body as we perceive, offers but little interest in its properties; but it is the more remarkable in its relation to hydrobenzöyl, from the fact, as analysis proves, that it has a perfectly similar composition, and is therefore an isomeric modification of the same, as is apparently shewn by its unintelligible origin from the oil, through the equally inexplicable action of potassa when air is excluded.

1.00 grm. of benzoin yielded by ignition, 2.860 grm. carbonic

---

[17] [Benzoin, $C_6H_5CH(OH)COC_6H_5$, can be formed from benzaldehyde only in the presence of a trace of cyanide, which was still present in Liebig and Wöhler's oil. Benzoin is a dimer of benzaldehyde. The two substances, therefore, have the same composition. Since chemists at the time did not accept Avogadro's hypothesis, they had no consistent way of determining molecular weights of organic substances and hence no criterion for distinguishing isomers from polymers.—O.T.B.]

acid and 0.512 of water. This gives its composition in one hundred parts;

Carbon,	79.079
Hydrogen,	5.688
Oxygen,	15.233

consequently the same (atomic) proportion of the same elements as in hydrobenzöyl.

It is indeed imaginable that the very different properties of benzoin and hydrobenzöyl arise from the manner of the hydrogen's combination, which in the first may be united to one atom of oxygen as water. But, as this difference depends on such a very different manner of the hydrogen's combination, the idea, that the hydrogen, can no longer as in the oil, be replaced by another body, as chlorine, seems to be refuted by the behavior of benzoin to bromine.

Thus if bromine be poured over it, it becomes heated and boiling and evolves hydrobromic acid in abundance. After this acid and the surplus of bromine are expelled by heat, the benzoin will be found changed to a brown viscous fluid, smelling like bromobenzöyl, but unlike the latter it is soft. With boiling water it appears to be decomposed either not at all or exceedingly slowly. With caustic potassa, it is indeed decomposed by boiling, but even then with difficulty. The alkaline solution mingled with hydrochloric acid deposites fine needle-form crystals, which do not appear to be benzoic acid, nor can they be unchanged benzoin, since they readily dissolve in alkali. Could we consider the above mentioned bromobenzoin, as an isometrical modification of the corresponding benzöyl compound, then were it imaginable that a new acid had formed by the above decomposition with alkali, which might be an isometric modification of benzoic acid.

We in vain endeavored to reconvert benzoin into hydrobenzöyl. Fused with hydrate of potassa, it changes like the oil into benzoic acid, with the evolution of hydrogen. But again it differs from the oil, in its behavior with a solution of potassa in alcohol. It is dissolved in the alkaline solution with a purple color, and presently the whole congeals to a mass of fine, foliated crystals. With water these form a milky fluid, from which by cooling after it has been heated, thick flakes of needle-form crystals are deposited, which are unchanged benzoin.

General Observations. Reviewing and collecting together the relations described in the present essay, we find that they all group around one single compound, which does not change its nature and composition in all its combining relations with other bodies. This stability, this consequence of the phenomena, induced us to consider that body as a compound base and therefore to propose for it a peculiar name, i.e. benzöyl.

The composition of this radical we have expressed by the formula $14C + 10H + 2O$.

In combination with one atom of oxygen, benzöyl forms dry benzoic acid, and in combination with one atom of oxygen, one of water, the crystallized acid.

In combination with two atoms of hydrogen, it constitutes pure bitter almond oil. When this oil changes in the air into Benzoic acid, it takes up two atoms of oxygen, one of which with the radical generates benzoic acid and the other with the two atoms of hydrogen forms the water of the crystallized acid.

Farther, the hydrogen of the oil or the oxygen of the acid may be replaced by chlorine, bromine, iodine, sulphur or cyanogen, and the bodies proceeding thence, comparable with the corresponding compounds of phosphorus, all form, by their decomposition with water, on the one side a hydracid, and on the other benzoic acid.

The replacement, of two atoms of hydrogen in the bitter almond oil by an acidifying base, appears to us in all cases a strong argument for adopting the opinion, that this hydrogen is in a peculiar manner combined with the other elements; this peculiar method of combination may be hinted at rather than pointed out by the idea of the radical, which is borrowed from inorganic chemistry.[18]

Although both benzamide and benzoin were originally in connection with the radical, they are wholly without its sphere, and must be considered as peculiar bodies, bearing no nearer relation to benzöyl, than urea to cyanogen.

Since we cannot compare the ternary base with cyanogen, because the greater number of elements must occasion far more complicated decompositions, and because they have no prevailing resemblance, we believe it not improbable, that there is more than one group of organic bodies, for example, the fluid oils, which may have this same radical as a compound basis. How far such a conjecture is correct may be ascertained by accurate analyses of other fluid oils in which the formation of benzoic acid, has been observed

---

[18] [De Morveau (1787) and Lavoisier had used the term radical as that portion of an anhydrous acid that was combined with oxygen. Liebig and Wöhler's benzoyl radical *contains* oxygen. Berzelius overlooked this in his first enthusiasm, but later suggested the oxygen be excluded from the radical of benzoic acid.— O.T.B.]

by mere oxidation in the air, or by action of nitric acid, particularly analyses of the oils of fennel-seed, anise-seed and cinnamon.

If an inference be allowed from the behavior of chloro and cyano-benzöyl, respecting the peculiar nature of the combination, which by the admission of water to the bitter almonds, causes the formation of prussic acid and hydrobenzöyl (crude oil of the bitter almonds), then it appears to us possible, without wishing to anticipate the experiment, that there is contained in the almonds a union of cyanogen with another body which is different from the hydrobenzöyl merely in the content of oxygen, so that by the admission of the constituents of water, hydrobenzöyl on the one side, and prussic acid on the other are formed; it farther seems to us probable, if amygdalin is a decomposition product of this combination with alcohol, that a similar exchange takes place as in the decomposition of chlorobenzöyl by alcohol, with this only difference that the cyanogen or its constituents enters into the new combination.

Benzoin in regard to its formation and physical properties possesses great similarity to the solid crystalline substances which are formed in other fluid oils; accurate analyses will unfold whether these (camphoroids)[19] are the same in composition with the fluid oils from which they proceed, and whether the cause of their different states or their other varying properties lies in the manner in which their constituents are combined.

Letter from Berzelius to Wöhler and Liebig Respecting Benzöyl and Benzoic Acid

Stockholm, Sept. 2, 1832.

Accept my thanks for the very interesting communication of your united and important researches respecting the bitter almond oil.

At your request I have examined my former experiments in regard to the composition of benzoic acid and find the result of your analysis wholly confirmed.

I have also made as you desired an analysis of benzoate of silver, and from 100 parts of the salt previously dried at 100° obtained by careful ignition, 46.83 gm. of metallic silver, which agrees as nearly as could be expected with the theoretical result calculated by you (46.86).

You have remarked that my analysis of benzoate of lead, perfectly agrees with the same. A later analysis made with sulphuric acid and alcohol gave the same result and consequently confirmed the atom of water of crystallization found in my first analysis.

I herewith transmit the result of an analysis made in 1813 of

---

[19] [The original reads *Kampferarten* (*stearoptene*).—O.T.B.]

sublimed benzoic acid, which I ignited in a tube with chlorate of potassa and chloride of potassium.

After this method 0.335 gm. of the acid yielded 0.138 gm. water and 0.855 of carbonic acid, which gives in one hundred parts;

Carbon, ... 68.85
Hydrogen, ... 4.99
Oxygen, ... 26.66

These numbers agree exactly with the composition of the hydrated acid $C^{14}H^{12}O^4$.

In vain did I endeavor to separate water from the benzoic acid,[20] by saturating the crystallized acid with a given quantity of oxide of lead, and therefore could not infer the presence of water of crystallization; this analysis farther gave four atoms of oxygen, although I had previously found by analysis of the salt of lead that the acid in it saturated three times as much of the oxide as in the neutral benzoate, I was therefore induced since the results did not correspond, to reject this analysis of the crystallized acid.

I next ignited given quantities of the neutral benzoate of lead, after endeavoring to free the same from water of crystallization by fusion.

Each analysed quantity of the salt was produced by itself; I have always followed the same principle, because a fault in one single operation may become a constant fault in every analysis; I therefore fused each portion of the salt by itself and always obtained varying results; the cause of which difference I believed must be ascribed to the volatilization of undecomposed benzoic acid. Upon now comparing the results of these analyses it is evident that different quantities of water still remained in the fused salt.

In order to prevent the volatilizing of the acid I employed the salt of lead; this is the analysis I have described. The result calculated from the corrected atomic weight and compared with your analysis is as follows;

	Result of the former.	Result of the correct analysis.
Carbon,	75.405	74.703
Hydrogen,	4.951	4.356
Oxygen,	19.644	20.941

The former analysis differs therefore from the theoretical composition by 0.702 carbon and 0.595 hydrogen, which overplus just as much diminished the oxygen.

---

[20] [The anhydrides of monocarboxylic acids, in contrast with those of dicarboxylic acids, are formed with great difficulty. They were first prepared by Gerhardt in 1852.—O.T.B.]

The results consequent upon your examination of the bitter almond oil, are the most important which vegetable chemistry has thus far received, and promise to diffuse an unexpected light over this part of science.

The circumstance that a body composed of carbon, hydrogen, and oxygen, combines with other bodies, particularly with such as form salts, after the manner of a simple body, proves that there are ternary composed atoms (of the first order) and the radical of benzoic acid is the first example proved with certainty, of a ternary body possessing the properties of an element. It is true indeed that we have before considered *sulphuret of cyanogen* (Schwefelcyan) as such, but you are aware that its combinations may be viewed as sulphurets and the body itself seems to be a sulphuret of cyanogen.

The facts proved by you give rise to such reflections, that we well may view them as the dawning of a new day in vegetable chemistry. I might for this reason propose to call the first discovered radical, composed of more than two elements, *proin* from πρωΐ dawn, in the sense ἀπὸ πρωΐ ἕως ἑσπέρως Acts xxviii. 20.) or *orthrin* (from ὀρθρὸς aurora,) from which the names *proic acid, orthric acid,* and *chloroproin, chlororthrin* can be employed with more facility. In consideration however, that the long received name benzoic acid would thereby become changed, and that we are always accustomed to respect names in general use where they do not embrace a double idea, by deriving new names from them, as *boron* from borax, potassium from potash, &c., it therefore appears to me in every respect more proper to employ the word proposed by yourselves and to change the term benzoic, into benzöylic acid.[21]

From the moment we know with certainty of the existence of ternary atoms of the first order, which combine after the manner of simple bodies, it will greatly facilitate expression in the language of formulas, to denote each radical by a peculiar sign, through which the idea of the combination to be expressed, instantly and clearly strikes the reader. I will illustrate this by a few examples. Thus if we put benzöyl $C^{14}H^{10}O^2 = Bz$, then we have,

$$\dot{B}z = \text{Benzöylic acid.}[22]$$
$$Bz\bar{H} = \text{Bitter almond oil.}$$
$$Bz\overline{Cl} = \text{Chlorobenzöyl.}$$

---

[21] We at first chose the name benzoin, as it properly stands in Berzelius' letter, and have since substituted the word benzöyl, that benzoin may be used for isometric hydrobenzöyl; by the ending in *yl*, we are the less reminded of strychnin, salicin, &c.—W. & L.

[22] [A line through a symbol represents a pair of atoms, a dot above a symbol an atom of oxygen, an apostrophe above a symbol, an atom of sulfur.—O.T.B.]

B′z or BzS = Sulphuret of benzöyl.[23]
Bz + 2N̶H̶³ = Ammoniuret of benzöyl, (benzöyl ammonia.)

If we put Amid = N̶H̶², we have

Bz + N̶H̶² = Benzamid or bitter benzöylamid.
C̶̈ + N̶H̶² = Oxamid.
K + N̶H̶² = Potassiumamid, (Berzelius' *Lehrbuch*, I. 794.)
Na + N̶H̶² = Sodium amid.

If we further place *oil of wine*, which I propose to call etherin,[24]

$$C^4H^8 = E,\text{ we find}$$
E + 2Ḣ = Alcohol.
E + Ḣ = Ether.
E + H̶C̶l = Muriatic ether.
E + N̈H̶ = Nitric ether.
E + BzḢ = Benzöylic ether.
ËS̈ + ḦS̈ = Sulphovinic acid according to Hennel and Serullas.
E + 2HS̈ = Sulphovinic acid according to Wöhler and Liebig.
2ËS̈ + Ḣ = Sulphuric oil of wine.
E + ĀḢ = Acetic ether.
2E + ĀH̶ = (Pyracetic spirit?) (Brenzessiggeist. German.)[25]
E + 2PtC̶l = Zeise's ethereal salt.
?E + 2Ṗt = Ethereal oxid of Platinum.
?E + 2Pt = Ether platinum.

Suppose by way of experiment, there is an oxid of etherine = E,
then [26] Ė + Ḣ = Ligneous spirit. (Holzspiritus. German.)
2Ė + Ḣ = Acetal or Doebereiner's new oxy-ether.

From these two last formulas, we perceive that acetal has the same relation to ligneous spirit, that pyroacetic spirit bears to acetic ether.

But I think it necessary to insist, that such formulas be employed only when the ideas they express, are advanced in some measure to confirm truths, else they would lead to a Babylonian confusion.

---

[23] It will be of great interest, to ascertain the behavior of this body to sulphurets.—B.

[24] [The etherin formulas refer to the work of Dumas and Boullay, *Ann. Chim.* 37, 15 (1828).—O.T.B.]

[25] ["Brenzessiggeist" is acetone, CH_3COCH_3. $\overline{A}$ represented the anhydride of acetic acid.—O.T.B.]

[26] According to the results of analyses of both bodies, which I sent by letter to Berzelius, and which will appear in one of the succeeding numbers of this Journal.—J.L.

2

Auguste Laurent

Translator's Preface (by William Odling); Carbon, Metallic and Hydrogen, Oxygen, and Chlorine Substitutions; Theory of Chlorine Substitutions; Nitrogen Substitutions

[From *Chemical Method, Notation, Classification, and Nomenclature*, London, Cavendish Society, 1855, v–viii and 180–205; translation (with new Preface) by William Odling of *Méthode de Chimie*, Paris, Mallet-Bachelier, 1854, 218–251. These sections summarize numerous papers by Laurent appearing in the *Annales de Chimie et de Physique* and in the *Comptes rendus de l'Académie des Sciences* in the years 1832 to 1852.]

Translator's Preface

The collection of the materials for this work extended over a considerable period of time, the subjects were arranged by the author when on his death bed, and the posthumous publication, with the revision of the proofs, was intrusted to the care of a friend. Under these circumstances, it is not surprising that some slight discrepancies should here and there exist; that a rigid uniformity of treatment, an exact adaptation of parts to one another, should occasionally be wanting.

Knowing that the majority of English students are almost unacquainted with Laurent's views; feeling the great importance of these views, and seeing how opposed they are to the opinions most prevalent in this country; I have endeavoured, while giving a clear and truthful representation of the author's meaning, to put his ideas in such a form as should least estrange the mind of the reader; and, by avoiding any confusion of symbols or want of uniformity in expression, have sought to render the work acceptable to as large a class of chemists as possible.

In the original work, four different systems of proportional weights are employed.

1°. The system of equivalents, ordinarily made use of in this country.

Hydrochloric acid	= HCl	Water	= HO
Chloride of sodium	= NaCl	Oxide of silver	= AgO.

2°. The atomic system of Berzelius, in which the proportional weights of hydrogen, nitrogen, chlorine, &c., are halved.

Hydrochloric acid	= H²Cl²	Water	H²O
Chloride of sodium	= NaCl²	Oxide of silver	= AgO

3°. The 4 volume system of Gerhardt, who employs Berzelius's weights for the non metallic, but halves the weights of the metallic elements, so as to make them correspond with hydrogen.

Hydrochloric acid	= H²Cl²	Water	= H²O
Chloride of sodium	= Na²Cl²	Oxide of silver	= Ag²O

The great majority of chemical compounds when expressed by these formulæ, correspond to 4 volumes of vapour. The exceptions are occasionally made to correspond by doubling; thus $H^2Cl^2 = 4$ vol. $H^4O^2 = 4$ vol.

4°. The 2 volume system of Gerhardt. This is the notation finally adopted by Laurent, and most generally employed throughout the work. The proportional weights of the elements are the same as in the preceding system, but all bodies (minus some few special exceptions) are represented by 2 volumes of vapour, thus: HCl, H^2O, $NaCl$, KHO, Ag^2O, NH^3, C^2H^6O, &c.

In the first of these systems, we have the ratios

	H	:	Cl	:	O
::	1	:	35·5	:	8
::	12·5	:	443·75	:	100

In the other three, we have the ratios

	H	:	Cl	:	O
::	1	:	35·5	:	16
::	6·25	:	221·87	:	100

The first ratio occurs but very seldom, and when it does, I have imitated the custom of Berzelius, and have placed a dash through the letters, H, Cl, N, &c. (H̶, C̶l̶, N̶), to indicate that these symbols express the proportional values usually employed in this country, and the doubles of those accorded to them in other parts of the book.

I have occasionally introduced a parenthetical observation, when I thought that some uncertainty might occur as to which of

the three systems was intended, thus (Berzelius's notation, ED.),
and now and then in elucidation of some other point, thus (Othyl,
ED.). Moreover, in some parts of the work, where the transitions
from the 4 volume to the 2 volume notation are very frequent, I
have represented the formulæ according to both systems.

The distinctions between the system of equivalents ordinarily
employed in this country, and the 2 volume notation adopted in
this work, may be thus expressed. In the new system, the atomic
weight of carbon is 12, of oxygen is 16, of sulphur is 32; and
similarly with selenium and tellurium; all the other atomic weights
are unaltered. The atomic expressions for all bodies not containing
carbon, oxygen, or sulphur, are unchanged; thus, H, N, HCl, KI,
NH^3, &c. When in an atomic formula the atoms of carbon,
oxygen, and sulphur, form even numbers, these numbers are
halved; thus, alcohol $C^4H^6O^2$ becomes C^2H^6O, ethyl C^4H^5
becomes C^2H^5, cyanogen C^2N becomes CN, &c. When the atoms
of carbon, oxygen, or sulphur, form uneven numbers, these numbers continue unchanged, while the number of the other atoms is
doubled; thus, sulphuric acid HSO^4 becomes H^2SO^4, water HO
becomes H^2O. It is observable, that though the atoms of hydrogen
and the radicals are respectively represented by H, Cl, C^2H^5, CN,
&c., their two-volume molecules consist of H.H, Cl.Cl, $C^2H^5.C^2H^5$,
CN.CN, &c.

Laurent has represented uranic, bismuthic, and other oxides,
sometimes as teroxides, sometimes as sesquioxides,—mercuric and
cupric oxides, sometimes as protoxides, sometimes as binoxides, a
proceeding which has led to some little confusion. For the sake of
uniformity, and in accordance with English custom, I have always
represented bismuthic oxide as a teroxide, uranic oxide as a ses-
quioxide, cupric and mercuric oxides as protoxides; whence a slight
change in the representation of some few formulæ has been occasioned. Laurent considering salts as derived from their acids by a
substitution of metal for hydrogen, has used indifferently the terms
sulphate of barium and sulphate of baryta, &c., a proceeding
which I have retained.

In the original work the signs, *plus*, *point*, and *parenthesis*, are indifferently made use of. Unless there was some reason to the
contrary, I have preferred making use of the *point* to indicate
combination, and the *plus* to indicate addition; thus I have preferred the second method of writing the succeeding equation, as
being more simple and more in accordance with English custom.

$$(C^4H^{10}O + C^4H^6O^3) + (KO + H^2O) = (KO + C^4H^6O^3) + (C^4H^{10}O + H^2O)$$
$$C^4H^{10}O.C^4H^6O^3 + KO.H^2O = KO.C^4H^6O^3 + C^4H^{10}O.H^2O$$

AUGUSTE LAURENT (1807–1853).   From *Revue Scientifique*, Vol. 72 (September 22, 1934), Paris.

Laurent generally gives the preference to empiric formulæ. In the earlier part of the book where rational formulæ are introduced for purposes of illustration, no definite sequence of symbols is adopted; thus O^3Fe^2, Fe^2O^3, OK, KO, are used indiscriminately. In the translation I have been more uniform, and have generally employed the arrangement most usual in this country.

Although adopting the above described slight alterations in expression, I am not conscious of having modified a single idea of the illustrious author's; and believing the generalities of Laurent to be in our day as important as those of Lavoisier were in his, I leave this translation in the hands of English chemists, in the earnest hope that it may tend to the substitution of that which is rational and experimental in chemical science, for that which is speculative and arbitrary.

I cannot conclude these remarks without thanking the Council of the Cavendish Society, and Mr. Graham in particular, for the confidence so kindly reposed in me as editor: nor must I neglect to apologize to the society for the delay which has occurred in the production of the work. This delay was caused partly by circumstances for which I am not responsible, and partly by the duties of an appointment of which I had no anticipation at the time of my undertaking this translation.

W O.

*　　*　　*

Carbon Substitutions. Carbon is perhaps the only elementary body which is without an analogue. To prove this assertion, we shall not refer to the important parts played by it and its compounds in the constitution of the earth, to its indispensable existence in all organised matters, vegetable and animal, nor to the important functions which, under the form of carbonic acid, it fulfils in the air and water; but we will, from a strictly chemical point of view, show that it is unparalleled by any other body.

In all treatises on chemistry, we find it compared, sometimes to hydrogen, sometimes to boron and silicon, but these associations are forced, and have reference but to one particular, the affinities of these bodies for oxygen; in other respects there is not the slightest analogy.

If we examine even the most simple combinations of carbon, its oxides, niturets, hydrurets, and chlorides,—among all other compound bodies, we shall not find any at all resembling them.

Lastly, we are not acquainted with any compound, which can

have its carbon replaced by some other simple body, and which, despite the permutation, will retain its principal properties. We might indeed compare the sulphites with the carbonates, or rather consider them as carbonates in which the carbon had been replaced by sulphur; but, on the one hand, this would be the only case in which the hypothesis would be admissible; and on the other hand, the sulphites do not bear any greater resemblance to the carbonates, than to the chlorites, to the sulphates, or to the majority of other salts.

Carbon substitutions, therefore, have no existence.

Metallic and Hydrogen Substitutions.   We need not inquire, whether or not certain metals, as zinc and potassium, can displace the hydrogen from certain acids, or in acting upon certain chloro- and iodo-combinations, can unite with the chlorine or iodine, and set at liberty bodies which are designated by the term compound radicals; we need only remember, that the majority of the metals play the parts one of another to a greater or less degree,—that we have placed hydrogen among the metals,—and that in our view, hydrogen is the representative of all the metals, that it is, so to say, *the* metal of organic chemistry; and we shall have occasion to bestow but a very secondary consideration upon the numerous metallic combinations.

Oxygen Substitutions.   Let us recall to our recollections, a primary fact, recognized in science for a long time past, namely, that oxygen, sulphur, selenium, and tellurium form a group of *equivalent* bodies;— of bodies which may replace one another mutually in their combinations, without altering the principal properties of the compounds into which they enter.

But can the above bodies likewise replace other bodies?—Are they the *equivalents* of chlorine, bromine, hydrogen, &c.?   All chemists, admit this equivalence, at least for chlorine and its analogues.   Let us see if this opinion is conformable to experience.

In comparing the phosphorous, phosphoric, silicic, benzoic, &c., chlorides, with the phosphorous, phosphoric, silicic, benzoic, &c., anhydrides, the comparison has had reference simply to the numerical composition of each of the terms.   According to the equivalent system of notation, the chlorides are represented as containing as many equivalents of chlorine, as the anhydrides contain equivalents of oxygen.

Chlorides .   .   . PCl^3, PCl^5, $SiCl$ $C^{14}H^5O^2Cl$;
Anhydrides   .   . PO^3, PO^5, SiO, $C^{14}H^5O^3$.

It has been observed also, that under the influence of water, the chlorides transform themselves into anhydrides, by an equivalent interchange of chlorine for oxygen, and from this metamorphosis, and from the above pointed out numerical correspondence, the analogy of the chlorides and anhydrides has been deduced.

We may remark in the first place, that there is an error in the numbers that have been compared, and that if we desire to be logical, we must write the formulæ of the chlorides and anhydrides in the following manner:

Chlorides .	.	.	P Cl^3	P Cl^5, SiCl^2,	C^7 H^5 O Cl,
Anhydrides	.	.	P^{2}O^3,	P^{2}O^5, SiO,	C^{14}H^{10}O^3;

We see that in this point of view the equality of the numbers no longer exists, and hence the transformation of the chlorides into anhydrides is but a hypothesis, springing naturally from the manner in which chemists have been accustomed to regard the combinations in question. Even if this transformation did take place, we should have no reason to conclude therefrom, that the chlorides and anhydrides resemble one another. But, in reality, the products of the transformation of the chlorides by water, are as follows:

Chlorides	.	.	PCl^3,	PCl^5, SiCl^2,	C^{7}H^{5}OCl, .
Products formed	.	PH^{3}O^3,	PHO^4, (SiO.xH^{2}O),	C^{7}H^{6}O^2;

which experimental results, are very different from the hypothetical ones.

But let us still further compare the chlorides with the anhydrides, let us see in what points they resemble one another. When put in the presence of the same reagent, I do not know of any case in which they comport themselves similarly. When placed in contact with oxides, or with salts, they behave in very different manners. When acted upon by ammonia, the chlorides decompose the alkali, the anhydrides unite with it, producing bodies analogous to sulphammon.

Moreover, Dutch liquid has no resemblance to aldehyde. Chloride of carbon, by the action of water, is not transformed into carbonic oxide; in one word, bibasic water does not resemble monobasic hydrochloric acid:

Let us now see, if oxygen may not in some cases be substituted for, or play the part of, hydrogen.

We have but few bodies, to which, even in a proportional number point of view, such a supposition would be applicable. The transformation of the alcohols into their corresponding acids, might however be adduced.

Wood spirit	.	.	.	C H^{4}O
Formic acid	.	.	.	C H^{2}O^2
Alcohol	.	.	.	C^{2}H^{6}O
Acetic acid	.	.	.	C^{2}H^{4}O^2, &c.

but as there is no analogy of properties between these acids and their alcohols, we cannot, from their analogy of composition, conclude that oxygen is the *equivalent* of hydrogen.

Oxygen being then the representative of sulphur, selenium, and tellurium, up to this time we have only carbon, hydrogen, and oxygen, as constituents of organic substances.

Let us say a few words concerning the action of oxygen upon organic substances. About fifteen years ago Dumas, in a law known as the *theory of substitutions*, endeavoured to define the action, which oxygen and chlorine exert upon organic substances.

Dividing all of them into two classes only, comprising the alcohols and hydrates in one division, and all the remaining organic substances in the other, he remarked, that these latter bodies when submitted to the action of chlorine or oxygen, always gained as many equivalents of chlorine and oxygen, as they lost equivalents of hydrogen.

This law, written under the influence of dualistic ideas, and at a period when but a very crude classification of bodies had been established, cannot be sustained at the present day. Even the examples then adduced by Dumas for the support of his law, now bear witness against it. Thus the transformations of the hydrides of benzoyl and cinnamyl into benzoic and cinnamic acids, being formulated thus:

$$C^{14}H^{12}O^2 + O^2 = C^{14}H^{10}O^3 + H^2O$$
$$C^{18}H^{16}O^2 + O^2 = C^{18}H^{14}O^3 + H^2O,$$

were considered by him as cases of substitution, but are in reality cases of addition, as seen below.

$$C^7H^6O + O = C^7H^6O^2$$
$$C^9H^8O + O = C^9H^8O^2,$$

whilst the alcohols, which he considered as hydrates, may, according to circumstances, exchange an equivalent of hydrogen for an equivalent of oxygen, or lose an equivalent of hydrogen without substitution. In chlorine substitutions however, we observe the frequent and remarkable fact, that the atoms of hydrogen set free, are exactly replaced by the same number of atoms of chlorine; such for example is the case with ether, which in losing 10 atoms of hydrogen, gains precisely 10 atoms of chlorine.

Even at the present day, it is impossible to define the action of oxygen upon organic substances. Some few remarks may nevertheless be made upon the subject.

Oxygen appears to be capable of combining directly or indirectly with certain hydro-carbons, which it transforms into aldehydes, and with certain aldehydes which it transforms into acids. The most general circumstance to be noted is, that oxygen, in oxidising bodies, tends to acidify them, and in superoxidising them tends to convert them into polybasic acids.

Thus alcohols and aldehydes become changed into acids, the former by losing hydrogen with substitution, the latter by a simple absorption of oxygen. Camphor, in uniting with three equivalents of oxygen, gives rise to bibasic camphoric acid; butyric acid, in exchanging one equivalent of hydrogen for two equivalents of oxygen, becomes bibasic; dialuric acid, by the absorption of an equivalent of oxygen, also becomes bibasic; it is the same with opianic acid, which, in taking up an equivalent of oxygen, is transformed into bibasic hemipinic acid. Lastly there are some substances which can lose hydrogen without substitutions; such are white indigo, hydrokinone, quinhydrone, Borneo camphor, &c.

Chlorine Substitutions. We have seen that fluorine, chlorine, bromine, and iodine, are the equivalents one of another, and we have refused to admit an equivalence between these bodies and oxygen. We now proceed to inquire, whether among the other simple bodies, there are any which should be associated with them.

When we cast a general glance at the metamorphosis produced by chlorine, in its action upon organic substances, we perceive the greatest variety.

Here, for example, are bodies which absorb 2, 4, or 6 atoms of chlorine without any loss; there, on the other hand, are bodies which lose hydrogen without any absorption of chlorine. Here are substances which lose successively 1, 2, 3, 4 . . . atoms of hydrogen, and acquire precisely the same number of atoms of chlorine; there are substances which having lost hydrogen, acquire sometimes more, sometimes less, than an equivalent proportion of chlorine.

But if, instead of examining organic substances in the mass, we divide them into several classes according to the functions which they fulfil, then we discover for some of these classes, a remarkable regularity in the manner in which chlorine comports itself with them.

Let us first of all examine the action of chlorine upon hydrocarbons, which I shall divide into hydro-carbons properly so called, and into hyperhydro-carbons.

Action of Chlorine upon the Hydrocarbons. From the experiments I have made upon this subject, I have deduced the following conclusions:

1°. *There are hydro-carbons which can absorb 2, 4, or 6 atoms of chlorine, without any loss of hydrogen.*

2°. *The hydrogen eliminated is always replaced, sometimes by its equivalent of chlorine, sometimes by more than its equivalent.*

Let us therefore divide the products of the action of chlorine upon the hydro-carbons, into two classes; the first containing the bodies in which the hydrogen lost, has been exactly replaced by its equivalent of chlorine; the second containing the bodies, which have simply absorbed chlorine, or which have absorbed a greater proportion thereof, than they have lost, of hydrogen.

To the first class let us give the name of *halydes*; to the second, that of *hyperhalydes*. If we take naphthaline as an example, the composition of the products obtained, will be as follows.

First class.

Naphthaline   . . . $C^{10}H^8$

$$
\text{Halydes} \quad . \quad . \quad . \quad
\begin{cases}
C^{10}H^7Cl \\
C^{10}H^6Cl^2 \\
C^{10}H^5Cl^3 \\
C^{10}H^4Cl^4 \\
C^{10}H^3Cl^5 \\
C^{10}H^2Cl^6 \\
C^{10}H\ Cl^7 \\
C^{10}\quad Cl^8
\end{cases}
$$

Second class.

$$
\text{Hyperhalydes} \quad . \quad . \quad
\begin{cases}
C^{10}H^8. \quad Cl^2 \\
C^{10}H^8. \quad Cl^4 \\
C^{10}H^7\ Cl.\ Cl^4 \\
C^{10}H^6\ Cl^2.Cl^4 \\
C^{10}H^5\ Cl^3.Cl^4
\end{cases}
$$

Let us now compare the properties of the halydes, with those of the hyperhalydes.

1°. All the halydes, however great the quantity of chlorine they contain, can be distilled without alteration.

2°. All the hyperhalydes, however small the quantity of chlorine they contain, are decomposed by distillation.

3°. All the halydes are undecomposable by potash.

4°. All the hyperhalydes are decomposable by potash.

5°. The hyperhalydes, either by distillation or by potash, invariably *lose* in the state of *chlorhydric acid*, *one half* of the chlorine absorbed, over and above the amount substituted for hydrogen. Thus the new product is invariably a halyde.

However, the hyperhalydes of the other hydro-carbons, are not always decomposed by distillation, especially when they are very volatile as is Dutch liquid; but in all cases, they are decomposed by potash.

It is clear that those hyperhalydes which no longer contain hydrogen, cannot lose the half of their chlorine in the state of chlorhydric acid; such for instance is the case with the perchloride of carbon C^2Cl^4. Cl^2; but this body when treated by sulphide of potassium, loses all its excess of chlorine, and consequently gives rise to the halyde C^2Cl^4.

Lastly, it may be remarked, that the bromine compounds do not behave exactly as do their chlorine analogues.

Thus, there are bromhyperhalydes, which, by distillation, lose bromine instead of bromhydric acid, but curiously enough, a halyde is nevertheless produced.

Let us adduce some examples of these different reactions.

	Hyperhalydes.			Halydes.
Naphthaline .	$C^{10}H^8$.	Cl^2 loses	$H\ Cl$ and produces	$C^{10}H^7Cl$
	$C^{10}H^8$.	Cl^4	H^2Cl^2	$C^{10}H^6Cl^2$
	$C^{10}H^6Cl^2$. Br^4		H^2Br^2	$C^{10}H^4Cl^2Br^2$
	$C^{10}H^6Cl^2$. Br^4		Br^2Br^2	$C^{10}H^6Cl^2$.
Benzine . .	$C^6\ H^6$.	Cl^6	H^3Cl^3	$C^6\ H^3Cl^3$
Etherine . .	$C^2\ H^4$.	Cl^2	$H\ Cl$	$C^2\ H^3Cl$
	$C^2\ H^3Cl$.	Cl^2	$H\ Cl$	$C^2\ H^2Cl^2$
	$C^2\ H^2Cl^2$.	Cl^2	$H\ Cl$	$C^2\ H\ Cl^3$
	$C^2\ H\ Cl^3$.	Cl^2	$H\ Cl$	$C^2\qquad Cl^4$
	$C^2\qquad Cl^4$.	Cl^2	$Cl\ Cl$	$C^2\qquad Cl^4$.

We may remark, that by treating the halydes with chlorine, the majority of them become transformed into hyperhalydes. But as these latter, by the influence of potash, become reconverted into halydes, it is clear that we can obtain the two series of halydes and hyperhalydes, from the same hydrocarbon, by treating it successively with chlorine and potash.

I take as an example etherine, the reactions of which, when submitted to this alternate treatment, I had pre-indicated. It is

to Regnault that we owe the experimental confirmation of what I
had advanced.[1]

---

[1] Immediately after my researches upon naphthaline, Regnault published a
memoir upon Dutch liquid.[2]   He shewed that this compound, by the action of
an alkali, loses the half of its chlorine, and he thence concluded, as I had done
with regard to the chlorides of naphthaline, that the formula of Dutch liquid,
ought to be represented thus: $C^4H^6Cl^2 + H^2Cl^2$.   Nevertheless an essential difference separated Regnault's manner of viewing the subject, from mine.   According to him, the first term is not (or was not) a representative or derivative of
bihydrocarbon C^4H^8,[3] but on the contrary, a chloride of aldehydene $C^4H^6 + Cl^2$.
Liebig having asserted that I obtained my notions concerning the naphthalic
chlorides[4] from this first memoir of Regnault, although my researches were published before those of this distinguished chemist, and the majority of chemists
having in their turns copied the assertion of Liebig, without in the least troubling
themselves as to its correctness, I feel myself warranted in transcribing in this place,
the note I published in the *Annales de Chimie et de Physique* immediately after the
appearance of the memoir on the chloride of aldehydene.

"In a memoir upon the combinations of bihydro-carbon with chlorine and
bromine, Regnault adduces the following experiment."

"*Condensed bromide of aldehydene* ($C^4H^6 + Br^2$) *was mixed with bromine in a flask,...;
after exposure to the sun it contained a liquid having a perfect resemblance to the bromo-
hydrocarbon* ($C^4H^8 + Br^4$) *; submitted to analysis it gave,*

Carbon	. . . .	9·38
Hydrogen	. . .	1·3
Bromine .	. . . .	89·32.

*We must then admit, that bromine, by its action upon the bromide of aldehydene, produces
bromo-hydrocarbon* ($C^4H^8 + Br^4$) *and bromhydric acid.*

"It is impossible to conceive how bromine, by abstracting hydrogen from
bromide of aldehydene, should produce a bromo-hydrocarbon, containing more
hydrogen than the bromide itself."   (I recalled here my views concerning the
chloro-hydrocarbons and added):

"We can have then four possible combinations, as results of the action of
bromine upon the bromide of aldehydene; $C^4H^4Br^4$, or $C^4H^4Br^4 + H^2Br^2$, or
$C^4H^2Br^6$, or $C^4H^2Br^6 + H^2 Br^2$.   By translating Regnault's analysis into formulæ
we have:

$$C^4H^4Br^4 + H^2Br^2.$$

	Calculated.	Found.
C^4	9·28	9·38
H^6	1·13	1·30
Br^6	89·59	89·32

---

[2] [Dutch liquid is ethylidene chloride CH_3CHCl_2.—O.T.B.]

[3] ["Bihydrocarbon C_4H_8" is ethylene C_2H_4.—O.T.B.]

[4] [This whole paragraph makes little sense once all formulas are halved to
convert them into their modern form.   Regnault claimed that Dutch liquid could
be considered an addition compound of $C_4H_6Cl_2$ and H_2Cl_2.   The argument
centers on the nature of $C_4H_6Cl_2$.   Regnault claimed it was an addition product
of Cl_2 and C_4H_6.   In modern terms this would correspond to a chlorine atom
added to the radical C_2H_3.   The latter is not a stable entity.   Laurent prefers
to consider $C_4H_6Cl_2$ as a substitution product of C_4H_8 (our C_2H_4, ethylene).
—O.T.B.]

	treated by chlorine		which treated by KHO
C^2H^4	produces	$C^2H^4.\ Cl^2$	produces
C^2H^3Cl	,,	$C^2H^3Cl.\ Cl^2$	,,
$C^2H^2Cl^2$	,,	$C^2H^2Cl^2.Cl^2$	,,
$C^2H\ Cl^3$	,,	$C^2H\ Cl^3.Cl^2$	,,
$C^2\ \ Cl^4$	,,	$C^2\ \ Cl^4.Cl^2$	,, [5]

All hydrocarbons do not give rise to hyperhalides. Turpentine and some others, lose hydrogen only by an equivalent substitution. The halydes formed in this manner, are equally unattackable by potash.

Action of Chlorine upon the Hyperhydrides. The hyperhydrides[6] are to the normal hydrocarbons, what the hyperhalydes are to the halydes. Thus there exists a compound of hydrogen and carbon, which may be represented as etherine *plus* hydrogen, $C^2H^4.H^2$, precisely as Dutch liquid is represented by this same etherine *plus* chlorine, $C^2H^4.Cl^2$.

"Some day we shall realize the following table:

No. 1	. . . . .	C^4H^8
2	. . . . .	$C^4H^6Cl^2 + H^2Cl^2$
3	. . . . .	$C^4H^6Cl^2$
4	. . . . .	$C^4H^4Cl^4 + H^2Cl^2$
5	. . . . .	$C^4H^4Cl^4$
6	. . . . .	$C^4H^2Cl^6 + H^2Cl^2$
7	. . . . .	$C^4H^2Cl^6$
8	. . . . .	$C^4\ \ Cl^8 + H^2Cl^2$
9	. . . . .	$C^4\ \ Cl^8$.

No. 4 will be obtained by treating No. 3 with chlorine; No. 5, by treating No. 4 with potash; No. 6, from No. 5 by chlorine; No. 7, from No. 6 by potash; and No. 8, from No. 7 by chlorine."

After that, I myself discovered numbers 6 and 7, and three or four years afterwards, Regnault completed the series.

It is in opposition to such glaring facts, that Liebig and his copyists have denied me all my rights, and have passed silently over all that I have done upon this subject. Some persons have said, that the merit in this case consists, not in the prevision of the facts, but in their experimental realization. Be it so, I will not argue upon such a subject. But, gentlemen, before distributing your rewards, you should first render justice; I ask for nothing more.[7]

[5] [These lines should be read as a continuous sentence.—O.T.B.]

[6] [The hyperhydrides are what we now call the fully saturated or alkane hydrocarbons. Laurent's "normal" hydrocarbons are the olefins C_nH_{2n}.—O.T.B.]

[7] [If we transcribe his ideas into modern formulas, Laurent is saying that the bromination of bromoethylene, C_2H_3Br, produces the tribromide $C_2H_3Br_3$. The analysis supports this view. This bromide can only be brominated further by *substitution*. Hydrogen bromide can then be removed by potash and more bromine added to take the place of the acid.—O.T.B.]

Let us see in what manner chlorine comports itself with the hyperhydrides; for example, with the hydruret of etherine.[8]

C^2H^6 $+ Cl^2$ gives rise to $C^2H^5Cl + HCl$ which is set free.

$C^2H^5Cl + Cl^2$	,,	$C^2H^4Cl^2 + HCl$	,,
$C^2H^4Cl^2 + Cl^2$	,,	$C^2H^3Cl^3 + HCl$	,,
$C^2H^3Cl^3 + Cl^2$	,,	$C^2H^2Cl^4 + HCl$	,,
$C^2H^2Cl^4 + Cl^2$	,,	$C^2H\ Cl^5 + HCl$	,,
$C^2H\ Cl^5 + Cl^2$	,,	$C^2\ \ \ Cl^6 + HCl$	,,

Thus, from the first to the last term, there is an equivalent substitution. We have compared the hyperhydrides to the hyperhalydes; this comparison is warranted by the action of potash upon their *derivatives*, which are thereby converted into halydes.

I call a chloro-compound a *derivative* of some other body, when its composition may be represented by that of the other body, *minus* hydrogen, *plus* an *equivalent* quantity of chlorine. Thus C^2H^5Cl is a derivative of C^2H^6,—C^2Cl^4 is a derivative of C^2H^4, and chloride of benzoyl, C^7H^5ClO, is a derivative of oil of bitter almonds, C^7H^6O. Since I first made use of this term, other chemists have employed it, but in another and very loose signification. Thus, according to them, Dutch liquid is a derivative of etherine, picric acid a derivative of indigo, &c. I retain the signification which I originally gave to the term, and thus when I say, that trichloracetic acid is a derivative of acetic acid, I mean, that this latter has lost three equivalents of hydrogen, and gained three equivalents of chlorine.

I ought not to close this subject without remarking, that marsh gas $CH^2.H^2$, the most simple of all the hyperhydrides, appears to comport itself differently from the rest of them. By the action of chlorine, it gives rise to the following derivatives CH^3Cl, CH^2Cl^2, $CHCl^3$, CCl^4; these, like the ordinary hyperhalydes, are decomposed by potash, but, in a different manner. Thus the compound $CHCl^3$ would be chloroform, and would consequently yield, by the action of potash, formic acid, CH^2O^2, instead of chloride of carbon, CCl^2; the compound CH^3Cl would be the chloride of methyl, and when acted upon by potash would give rise to methylic alcohol.[9]   Never-

---

[8] [Hydruret of etherine: hydride of ethylene, i.e. ethane.—O.T.B.]

[9] [Laurent has become aware of a characteristic difference between compounds containing one and those containing several carbon atoms. The latter lose HCl from chloroderivates more easily because, as we now know, the H and Cl are lost from adjacent carbon atoms leaving a double bond $C=C$. When only a single carbon atom is present the loss of HCl would produce an entity with only partially satisfied valences. The formation of the intermediate CCl_2, chlorocarbene, has only recently been demonstrated (cf. J. Hine, *Physical Organic Chemistry*, New York, McGraw-Hill, 1956, pp. 131–2).—O.T.B.]

theless I ought to remark, that the experiments made upon this subject require to be repeated.

I may observe generally, that the bodies of the most simple series, that which contains but one atom of carbon, not unfrequently comport themselves differently from the corresponding terms of the superior series, as we shall presently see exemplified in the case of formic acid.

Action of Chlorine upon the Aldehydes. Aldehydes homologous with ordinary aldehyde, as well as those analogous to hydruret of benzoyl, when submitted to the action of chlorine, lose hydrogen, with equivalent substitution only. Thus ordinary aldehyde produces successively

$$C^2H^4 \quad O + Cl^2 = C^2H^3Cl \; O + HCl \text{ set free}$$
$$C^2H^3Cl \; O + Cl^2 = C^2H^2Cl^2O + HCl \quad ,,$$
$$C^2H^2Cl^2O + Cl^2 = C^2H \; Cl^3O + HCl \quad ,,$$
$$C^2H \; Cl^3O + Cl^2 = C^2 \quad Cl^4O + HCl \quad ,,$$

The chlor-aldehydes[10] are attackable by potash, but this reagent does not simply remove chlorhydric acid from them, as from the hyperhalydes, but by virtue of an equation similar to the following, converts them into the state of acids:

$$C^7H^5ClO + H^2O = C^7H^6O^2 + HCl.^{11}$$

Action of Chlorine upon the Acids, Respectively Homologous with Acetic, and Analogous to Benzoic Acid. All these acids, when they lose hydrogen, invariably acquire equivalent proportions of chlorine. Thus acetic acid gives rise to chloracetic acid,

$$C^2H^4O^2 + 3Cl^2 = C^2Cl^3HO^2 + 3HCl.$$

It is worthy of remark, that despite the greater or less substitution of chlorine, the saturating capacities[12] of the acids, continue unaltered.

Formic acid, the most simple of all, comports itself differently

---

[10] [By chlor-aldehydes, Laurent means acid chlorides RCOCl. His equation refers to benzoyl chloride: $C_6H_5COCl + H_2O \rightarrow C_6H_5CO_2H + HCl$—O.T.B.]

[11] After the example of Gerhardt, I nearly always replace potash by water in my equations, by which means, acids instead of (what comes to much the same thing) potash salts, appear to be produced. To avoid confusion, it is sufficient to be warned of the convention.

[12] [By saturating capacity is meant the extent to which it acts as an acid, i.e. its neutralizing capacity.—O.T.B.]

from the rest, being decomposed into chlorhydric and carbonic acids,

$$CH^2O^2 + Cl^2 = CO^2 + 2HCl.$$

Up to this time, we have not succeeded in completely de-hydrogenising an acid, by substitution; thus trichloracetic acid still retains one atom of hydrogen, as does likewise the pentachloro-phenic acid. It would seem from this, that in the formation of a salt, it is this last atom which is exchanged for the metal: neverthe-less, the impossibility of removing this last atom of hydrogen by a substitution of chlorine, is not anywhere proved, and we know well, that the more hydrogen a body has lost, the more difficult it is to remove the remainder.

It would be interesting to study the action of chlorine upon the trichloracetate of silver, to see if we should have, as with the ben-zoate of silver,

$$C^2Cl^3AgO^2 + Cl^2 = C^2Cl^4O^2 + AgCl.$$

In this case we might inquire, whether the quadrichloracetic acid could be an acid. The reply would depend upon our definition of an acid. If an acid is a body containing hydrogen, and by an ordinary double decomposition capable of exchanging its hydrogen for a metal, it is clear that quadrichloracetic acid could no longer be considered as an acid.

But if an acid is a body which can exchange one of its elements for a metal, so as to form a salt of the metal, then quadrichloracetic acid might well be an acid. If when put in the presence of hydrate of potash, it gave rise to trichloracetate of potash,

$$C^2Cl^4 \ O^2 + KHO$$
$$= C^2Cl^3KO^2 + ClHO$$

the reaction would be similar to that afforded by trichloracetic acid, with the same alkali,

$$C^2Cl^3HO^2 + KHO$$
$$= C^2Cl^3KO^2 + HHO,$$

and no one could refuse to consider it as an acid.

Nevertheless the two reactions would not correspond so closely as the two equations seem to indicate, because the hypochlorous acid, ClHO, or mono-chloruretted water, produced in the one instance, would give rise to a secondary reaction.

Action of Chlorine upon the Other Acids. We have no exact know-ledge upon this subject. Nevertheless we might foresee, that complex acids, such as the sulphanilic, sulphonaphthalic, camphovinic, &c., would undergo equivalent substitutions, or would give rise to products, procurable by acting separately upon sulphuric acid, camphoric acid, aniline, naphthaline, and alcohol, by chlorine.

Action of Chlorine upon the Alkaloids. Two principal cases may present themselves, accordingly as the product of the action of chlorine is an alkaloid or a neutral body.

In the latter case we have a simple equivalent substitution, as is the case with ammonia and aniline.

$$H^3N + 3Cl^2 = Cl^3 N \quad + 3HCl$$
$$H^3N + 2I^2 = HI^2N \quad + 2HI$$
$$C^6H^7N + 3Cl^2 = C^6H^4Cl^3N + 3HCl.$$

In the former case, the chlorine might at first sight appear to combine simply with the alkaloid; as, for instance, when chlorine acts upon codeine, we obtain

$$C^{18}H^{21}NO^3 + Cl^2 = C^{18}H^{21}NO^3Cl^2,$$

and with cinchonine,

$$C^{19}H^{22}N^2O + Cl^4 = C^{19}H^{22}N^2OCl^4.$$

But what really takes place in these instances is this: the codeine undergoes a chlorine substitution, and gives rise to a basic chloro-codeine, with which the hydrochloric acid continues combined.

$$C^{18}H^{21}NO^3 + Cl^2 = C^{18}H^{20}ClNO^3.HCl.$$

so that when potash is added to the salt, monochloro-codeine is precipitated.

With cinchonine the reaction is analogous, bichloro-cinchonine is formed, and the two equivalents of chlorhydric acid remain in combination with the new base.

$$C^{19}H^{22}N^2O + Cl^4 = C^{19}H^{20}Cl^2N^2O. H^2Cl^2.$$

Nevertheless codeine would appear to comport itself differently with iodine: according to Anderson it produces simply an iodide of codeine containing $C^{18}H^{21}NO^3. I^3$, from which, codeine is regenerated by the action of potash. I cannot admit such a formula, firstly on account of the uneven number of its dyads,[13] secondly, because the reactions of the substance are inconceivable.

---

[13] [Dyads: Elements whose atoms normally exist paired, e.g., H_2, HCl, Cl_2, N_2.—O.T.B.]

Action of Chlorine upon the Alcohols.   According to Dumas, these bodies lose at first two atoms of hydrogen without substitution; and then, for every subsequent displacement of an atom of hydrogen, acquire an equivalent of chlorine.   This is the same as saying, that the alcohols are firstly transformed into aldehydes, upon which the chlorine then acts by substitution.   Despite the researches that have been made upon this subject, we are far from knowing exactly what takes place, when we treat with chlorine, I do not say the alcohols, but even ordinary vinic alcohol.[14]

For if aldehyde is formed, chlorhydric acid must be disengaged, and this latter in the presence of alcohol, should produce chlorhydric ether and water.   Under the influence of this water, the chlorine might transform a part of the alcohol into acetic acid, and consequently give rise to acetic ether.[15]   Chlorine in acting upon all these products, ought to convert them into chlorhydric ether, more or less chlorinated, and even into perchloride of carbon,—into aldehyde, acetic acid, and acetic ether, more or less chlorinated.

Wood spirit gives products, of which the formation is far from being explained.   Thus, according to Kane, Weidman, Schweizer and Bouis, we may have formed: $C^6H^4Cl^2O^2$, $C^{12}H^{16}Cl^8O^3$, $C^{12}H^{16}Cl^{10}O^5$, $C^3H^3Cl^3O$, $C^5H^{10}Cl^2O^2$, $C^3H^2Cl^4O + 4Aq$, &c., &c.

Action of Chlorine upon the Ethers.   Having had occasion to examine the action of chlorine upon the acetate of methyl, and having seen that for each atom of hydrogen set free, an equivalent of chlorine was absorbed, I concluded that the acetate of methyl, despite its change of composition, retained its primary constitution.   Since this first experiment, Malaguti has examined the subject with much care, and has shown, that nearly all the ethers undergo equivalent substitutions; although, according to him, pyromucic ether absorbed four atoms of chlorine without loss of hydrogen.   We can conceive, that some of these complex combinations may occasionally divide themselves, and thus disturb the substitutions.   Acetic ether for instance, when its saturation by chlorine is nearly arrived at, splits up into two molecules, and becomes metamorphosed into perchloride of carbon, which is not a derivative of acetic ether.

With formate of methyl on the other hand, the combination rises in the scale, for the two carbon groups which form this ether, unite into one, so as to produce here likewise, per-chloride of carbon.

---

[14] [Vinic alcohol: ethyl alcohol.—O.T.B.]
[15] [Acetic ether: ethyl acetate.—O.T.B.]

Action of Chlorine upon Various Compounds. Among other compounds, there exist a great many which, like isatine, undergo equivalent substitutions; there are also others, such as white indigo, benzoine, hydro-kinone, &c., which may lose hydrogen without substitution, or else gain less of chlorine than they have lost of hydrogen. At present we are unable to formulate any law upon the subject.

Theory of Chlorine Substitutions. The first fact which struck me in these substitutions, was the stable condition of equilibrium of the halydes: I perceived these molecular groups reappear incessantly, from the midst of the successive transformations of the first term; I perceived these groups, however great the quantity of chlorine they contained, resist, contrarily to all previous experience, the action of alkalies.

The instability of the hyperhalydes was not less striking, for all these bodies, however minute the quantity of chlorine they contained, were, on the contrary, attackable by alkalies.

The next circumstance which astonished me still more, was to see the halydes, hyperhalydes, acids, ethers, alkaloids, and numerous other bodies, conserve their fundamental properties throughout the transformations effected by the action of chlorine,—to see certain bodies lose but 1 or 2 per cent. of hydrogen, and gain fifty or sixty per cent. of chlorine or bromine, and yet bear to the bodies from which they were derived, a greater resemblance than is borne by sulphate of iron to sulphate of potash.

Formerly I expressed these facts by saying, that chlorine, a body so different from hydrogen, might, under certain circumstances, take its *place* and fulfil its functions, without changing the arrangement of the atoms of the compounds into which it entered.

To render my idea more intelligible, I made the following comparison.

"Let us imagine a four-sided prism, of which the eight angles are occupied by eight atoms of carbon, and the centres of the twelve edges by twelve atoms of hydrogen. Let us call this prism the *form* or *fundamental nucleus*, and let us represent it by

$$C^8H^{12}.$$

"If to the bases of the prism, we apply pyramids or atoms of hydrogen, we shall have a hyperhydride,—if of chlorine, a hyperhalyde,—and if of oxygen, an aldehyde or acid. We will represent the form and composition of these pyramidal prisms thus:

$$C^8H^{12} + H^2$$
$$C^8H^{12} + Cl^2$$
$$C^8H^{12} + O$$
$$C^8H^{12} + O^2.$$

"By certain reactions, we shall be able to slice away the pyramidal portions of the crystal, that is to say, take away its chlorine, oxygen, or excess of hydrogen, and re-obtain the fundamental prism.

"Let us suppose that chlorine, put in presence of this simple prism, removes one of the edges or hydrogen atoms; the prism deprived of this edge would be destroyed, unless it were supplied with some other edge, whether of chlorine, bromine, zinc, &c.; no matter what the nature of the edge, provided it succeeds in maintaining the equilibrium of the other edges and angles. Thus will be formed a new or *derived nucleus* similar to the preceding, and of which the form may be represented by

$$C^8(H^{11}Cl).$$

"If we put this new prism in the presence of chlorine, we may pyramidise it, that is to say, transform it into a hyperhalyde,

$$C^8(H^{11}Cl) + Cl^2;$$

or we may remove from it, another edge of hydrogen. But this, must be still replaced by an edge of chlorine, and we shall obtain a new derived prism of which the formula will be

$$C^8(H^{10}Cl^2).$$

"With this prism and chlorine, bromine or iodine, we may construct, either other derivatives, or other hyperhalydes; and with oxygen, aldehydes, and acids. The formulæ of all these new prisms derivative and pyramidal, will be represented in the following manner:

Halydes.	Hyperhalydes.	Aldehydes.	Acids.
$C^8H^{10}Cl^2$	$C^8H^{10}Cl^2 + Cl^2$	$C^8H^{10}Cl^2 + O$	$C^8H^{10}Cl^2 + O^2$
$C^8H^6 Cl^6$	$C^8H^6 Cl^6 + Cl^2$	$C^8H^6 Cl^6 + O$	$C^8H^6 Cl^6 + O^2$
$C^8H^4 Cl^4 Br^4$	$C^8H^4 Cl^4 Br^4 + Cl^2$	$C^8H^4 Cl^4 Br^4 + O$	$C^8H^4 Cl^4 Br^4 + O^2$
$C^8 \quad Cl^{12}$	$C^8 \quad Cl^{12} + Cl^2$	$C^8 \quad Cl^{12} + O$	$C^8H \quad Cl^{11} + O^2$

"Chlorine, bromine, oxygen, &c., in excess, completely alter the properties of the fundamental nucleus and its derivatives, whilst the chlorine, bromine, and iodine, which enter into the various nuclei, do not destroy the principal properties of the original substance. Each nucleus, however little or much chlorinated, is capable of forming a hyperhalyde by the absorption of chlorine, an aldehyde or an acid by the absorption of oxygen. It is then to the position occupied by, and not to the nature of, the chlorine, that we must attribute the resistance it offers to the action of alkalies. Thus the chlorine of the nuclei, resists the action of heat and alkalies; whilst the chlorine in excess, under the influence of one or other of these agents, seizes upon one of the hydrogen edges of the nucleus, to become disengaged in the form of chlorhydric acid, at the same time that another portion of the excess of chlorine, takes the place of the hydrogen that has been set free. Thus it is necessary, that in the hyperhalydes, the excess of chlorine should always present an even number."

Whether or not the halydes exist as such in the hyperhalydes, aldehydes, and chloracids, is a matter of but little consequence. Whatever atomic arrangement we may please to imagine, we cannot destroy the fact, that certain substances may experience chlorine substitutions without losing their fundamental properties.

Such are the ideas enunciated by me some time since, upon the subject of substitutions, by which ideas chemists were so greatly scandalized.

To have compared nitrogen with antimony, with boron, or even with chlorine, might up to a certain point have been conceivable, but to imagine that chlorine, the most negative of all bodies, could fulfil the functions of the highly positive hydrogen, was to misunderstand the most elementary notions of chemistry.

The first attack started from Giessen. Liebig criticised not only the ideas I had made known, but also the analyses on which they were founded. He therefore proposed other formulæ, and thought fit to accompany them with cutting personalities. Unfortunately for Liebig, it was shown that all the corrections he had made, were themselves incorrect. This was the first check to dualism.

Malaguti then made known his excellent researches upon the chloro-ethers. I seized this occasion to return to the question of substitutions, and I maintained, that the ethers in becoming chlorinated, still continued ethers. I do not know, said I, what the arrangement of the atoms of acetic ether really is; whether $(C^4H^6O^3 + C^4H^{10}.O)$ or $(C^4H^6O^3 + C^4H^8 + H^2O)$ or $(C^4H^8O^4 + C^4H^8)$ &c., I cannot tell; but I maintain, that be the arrangement what it may, it continues the same in the chlorine derivatives.

In reply to the question, what is meant by the words: "The chloro-ether continues an ether?" I might repeat, what I have just said, namely, that the arrangement of its atoms is the same as that of the normal ether. But I prefer to leave hypotheses aside, and say simply, that an ether is a body obtained by the reaction of an acid upon an alcohol, with an elimination of water, and that under certain circumstances the ether can be divided, either by regenerating the alcohol and acid which gave it birth, or by forming products which belong to the families of the alcohol and of the acid; as if indeed the ether were formed of two groups, the one containing a part of the elements of the alcohol, the other a part of the elements of the acid.

Well then, certain chlor-ethers can be obtained by the reaction of chloracids upon alcohols, with a similar elimination of water; and nearly all these chlor-ethers when submitted to the action of anhydrous ammonia, of an alcohol, of potash, and even of heat, divide themselves into products belonging to the families of the acid and of the alcohol which served to produce them. Thus acetic ether for example, gives origin to acetamide; chloracetic ether to chloracetamide, &c. Numerous examples of these changes may be seen in a very lucid résumé, that has been published upon this subject by Gerhardt.

The labours of Malaguti excited Berzelius to undertake the defence of dualism. Relying upon pure hypothesis indeed, and treating from the summit of his grandeur, the ideas which had been emitted upon the subject, he showed, that the notion of substitutions was contrary to common sense. In his hands, the mono-, bi-, and tri-, chloro-naphthalines were transformed into the chloride of icodecatesseryle, chloride of decahexyle, and chloride of decapentyle. Chloride of benzoyl C^7H^5ClO became a benzoic oxy-chloride $2 (C^{14}H^{10}O^3) + (C^{14}H^{10}Cl^3)$.

The whole of chemistry was simplified in the same fashion.

Berzelius having confounded the *law of substitutions*, with the remarks, the generalities, and the theory that I had published, Dumas took advantage of the opportunity, to reject all consistency between his opinions and mine, by saying, *that his theory was no theory at all* (which is the truth), *but only an empirical law, expressive of a simple relation between the hydrogen eliminated, and the chlorine absorbed—nothing more*.

Nevertheless some years after, Dumas made the discovery of trichloracetic acid. Astonished at seeing, that acetic acid and its derivative had the same capacity of saturation, the same volume, were decomposed in an analogous manner under the influence of baryta, yielded each of them an ether, &c., he adopted my opinion, saying, that in the two acids the arrangement of the atoms must be the same, that the acids in fact, belonged to the same type.[16]

---

[16] I perceive in several works on chemistry, that many persons do not understand the difference that exists, between Dumas's ideas and mine concerning substitutions, notwithstanding that they are altogether dissimilar.

The notion of substitutions, if we understand thereby, as we ought to understand, the replacement of chlorine, by bromine, iodine, and fluorine, or the replacement of silver, by copper, iron, or potassium, is as ancient as are the ideas of Richter and Wenzel upon the decomposition of salts. We have known for a long time that the simple bodies displace one another mutually from their combinations, most generally by exchanging equivalent for equivalent, but not unfrequently in a different manner.

We have known that chlorine, by its action upon certain organic substances, as cyanhydric acid, essence of bitter almonds, wax, &c., expels a certain number of atoms of hydrogen, which are replaced by an equal number of atoms of chlorine. We have known that oxygen sometimes comports itself in a similar manner, and also, that in some bodies the hydrogen set free is not replaced by its equivalent of chlorine.

Two questions present themselves: 1°. Can we know *à priori*, whether the hydrogen set free, will or will not be replaced by its equivalent of chlorine, and how much of it may be liberated without substitution? 2°. What becomes of the chlorine in the new chloro compounds; what function does it fulfil; of what nature are the compounds into which it enters, either by an equivalent, or a nonequivalent substitution?

These two questions are, we perceive, altogether independent of each other. We might discover the law presiding over substitutions, without knowing what takes place within the chloro-compounds, and *vice versá*.

Dumas confined himself to the first question, and under the name of the theory of substitutions (he himself remarked that he ought to have said *law* of substitutions) he announced the two following propositions.

1°. *When we treat an organic substance by chlorine, bromine, iodine, or oxygen, these bodies generally set free hydrogen, and for one equivalent of hydrogen liberated, there is retained in the compound one equivalent of chlorine, bromine, iodine, or oxygen.*

2°. *If a part of the hydrogen of the organic substance, exists in the state of water (as in alcohol), it will be set free by the chlorine or oxygen, without substitution.*

The law is precise, and void of ambiguity: I do not purpose to inquire whether or not it is correct (*vide*, what I have said concerning chlorine and oxygen substitutions in this and the preceding chapter respectively). All that I have to say is, that I have not adopted this law, and that I have myself formulated certain propositions which are altogether different, and are applicable, almost solely to the hydro-carbons. I then have nothing whatever to claim in the above *law* of substitutions. It belongs entirely to Dumas.

With regard to the second question, Dumas never concerned himself with it, unless indeed, after I had done so. It is this subject that I have for a long time had in view in my researches (*vide* my opinion thereon in this chapter); it is in reference to it, that I have advanced the following proposition: *when there is* EQUIVALENT *substitution of chlorine or bromine for hydrogen, the chlorine actually takes the* PLACE *that was occupied by the hydrogen, and to a certain degree, fulfils the functions thereof, consequently the chloro-compound must be analogous with the compound from which it was derived.*

Thus there is but little analogy between my opinion, my propositions—and the law of Dumas. Here is the reply of this illustrious chemist to Berzelius, by whom he had been rendered somewhat responsible for my extravagances. "Berzelius attributes to me, an opinion precisely contrary to that which I have always maintained, namely, that the chlorine in this case[17] takes THE PLACE of the hydrogen. I have never said anything of the kind, neither can anything of the kind be deduced from the opinions I have put forward with regard to this order of facts. To represent me as saying, that hydrogen is replaced by chlorine, which fulfils the same functions, is to attribute to me an opinion against which I protest most strongly, as it is opposed to all that I have written upon these matters. The law of substitutions is an empiric law and nothing more; it expresses a relation between the hydrogen expelled, and the chlorine retained. I am not responsible for the gross exaggeration with which Laurent has invested my theory; his analyses moreover do not merit any confidence."

Dumas and I made use of the same word substitution, from which circumstance arose much of the confusion that prevails on this subject. This confusion was still further augmented, by our employment of special terminations in *ase*, *ese*, and *ise*, &c., terminations *conceived by Dumas* as expressive of the relation between the number of hydrogen atoms liberated, and the number of other atoms retained, but *employed by me* to indicate that the chloro-compound *in the case of an equivalent substitution*, must still preserve the constitution of the original substance.

Thus Dumas represented the constitution of essence of canella[18] by this formula: $C^{18}H^{14}O^2 + H^2$; that of chloride of cinnamyl by this: $C^{18}H^{14}O^2 + Cl^2$; and the *composition* of chlorocinnose[19] (= the hydride $- 4H^2 + 4Cl^2$) by $C^{18}H^8Cl^8O^2$, observing that he called the body *chlorocinnose provisionally*, inasmuch as he did not know how to represent its molecular constitution, nor with what body to compare it.

My opinion was very different. If I had considered essence of canella as forming a unique molecule $C^{18}H^{16}O^2$, and had named it cinnamyl, I should have called the chloro-compound, *chlorocinnose*. If I had regarded the essence as a hydride $C^{18}H^{14}O^2 + H^2$, I should have named the chloro-compound *chloride of chlorocinnose* $C^{18}H^8Cl^6O^2 + Cl^2$: If I had considered the essence as a hydrate of cinnamyl $C^{18}H^{14}O + H^2O$, I should have called the chloro-compound *hydrate of chlorocinnose* &c., &c.

Thus despite the similitude of the terminations, despite the same values ascribed to the same vowels by Dumas and myself, there is not any analogy between the ideas which these two nomenclatures represent, excepting, that they both express the quantity of hydrogen set free, and the quantity of chlorine fixed.

I will adduce the following examples, to show the absolute difference that exists between my opinion and that of Dumas.

Dumas represented alcohol by $C^4H^8 + H^4O^2$, and acetic acid by $C^4H^6O^3 + H^2O$ and nevertheless saw a case of substitution in the conversion of the first into the second:

$$\text{Alcohol} - 2H^2 + 2O = \text{acetic acid.}$$

Since at that time, Dumas maintained that alcohol contained 2 atoms of water, while acetic acid contained only one, it is clear that in his law of substitu-

---

[17] I had just made the chlorhydrate of chloretherise, and an acetate of chloromethylene. I maintained that the first body had the same constitution as Dutch liquid, and that in the second, the atoms were disposed exactly as in the acetate of methylene. It was in reference to this opinion, that Berzelius chose to render Dumas responsible for my errors.

[18] [Essence of canella: cinnamaldehyde $C_6H_5CH{=}CHCHO$.—O.T.B.]

[19] [Chlorocinnose: a chloride of cinnamaldehyde.—O.T.B.]

Then Berzelius, placing the question upon its real footing, though but for a moment, examined if the properties of the chloro derivative, really did resemble those of acetic acid; he pronounced for the negative, and in consequence, attributed to each of the acids a different atomic arrangement, and represented their composition thus:

Normal acetic acid . . $C^4H^6. O^3 + H^2O$

Trichloracetic acid . . $C^2O^3 + H^2O + C^2Cl^6,$

which latter body was in his opinion, a combination of oxalic acid with an unknown oxalic chloride.

In reply to Berzelius, the resemblance of the halydes to each other, and of the hyperhalydes to each other, was pointed out. It was shown that the chlorethers divided themselves into products appertaining to the families of the acids and the alcohols from which they had been formed, that the two acetic acids have the same capacity of saturation, &c.; and lastly, that in all compounds, the chloro-derivatives retain the same volume as the normal substances from which they were derived. But Berzelius rejected all these ties of community, and persisted in arranging normal substances, in positions most opposite to those of their chloro-derivatives.

About this time, Wœhler entered the lists; but, more courteous than his brethren in arms, contented himself with lancing jocularities against the theory of substitutions.

He said, that by treating sulphate of manganese with chlorine, he had succeeded in replacing successively, the manganese, sulphur, and even the oxygen, by chlorine, and had thus obtained a chlorosulphate of manganese, which contained neither manganese, nor oxygen, nor sulphur, and which was nevertheless a sulphate.[20]

Though less skilful than Wœhler, I endeavoured to imitate his marvellous discovery, and proceeded as follows: I treated isatine

---

tions, he considered only the ratio between the hydrogen liberated, and the chlorine or oxygen fixed, without pretending that the primitive and the derived body, belonged to the *same type.*

This is rendered still more evident by the following examples, which Dumas brought forward in support of his law.

Alcohol $-4 H^2 + 4O =$ formic acid,

Acetic acid $-2 H^2 + 2O =$,,   ,,

It is certain that Dumas, notwithstanding the equivalent substitution, did not consider alcohol, acetic acid, and formic acid, as belonging to the same type.

It was some considerable time after this, when he had discovered the chloracetic acid, that he adopted my opinion concerning the functions of chlorine in substitution compounds, which view he extended so as to include oxygen, although I had myself ceased to apply it to this last body.

[20] [Cf. p. 5.—O.T.B.]

by chlorine and by bromine; I procured derivatives which contained from 25 to 50 per cent. of chlorine and bromine, in the place of 1 and 2 per cent. of hydrogen. And in despite of this enormous difference in the centesimal composition, despite the loss of the highly positive hydrogen, and the substitution of the highly negative chlorine, here are the changes which the isatine had undergone:

Isatine.	Chlorisatine.	Bichlorisatine.
Orange red	idem.	
Prisms of 113°	id.	of 114°.
Sublimes in part without decomposition . . .	id.	
Very slightly soluble in water	id.	
Moderately soluble in alcohol and ether . .	id.	
Yellow solutions	id.	
With potash, at first exchanges H for K . .	id.	
The potassic salt is of a reddish black . . .	id.	
With silver salts, it gives a precipitate like the dregs of wine	id.	
It is very unstable, and quickly absorbs H²O to form isatinate of potash	id. chloro.	
This new salt is yellow	id.	
By the action of acids, it regenerates isatine . .	id. chloro.	
Isatine decomposed by sulphide of ammonium, absorbs hydrogen, forming isathyde . . .	id. chloro.	
This last body occurs in whitish scales . . .	id.	
It is transformed according ⎰ into crimson indine .	id. chloro.	
to circumstances . . ⎱ or into isatine . .	id. chloro.	
Ammonia forms with ⎧ a grey amide . .	id. chloro.	
isatine . . . . . ⎨ a yellow amide . .	id. chloro.	
⎩ a scarlet amidic acid	id. chloro.	
The isatinate of ammonia is transformed by evaporation into a yellow isamate	id. chloro.	
This isamate by desiccation, forms a yellow isamide	id. chloro.	
The isamate and isamide, by the action of acids, produce either isamic acid or isatine . . .	id. chloro.	
Isatine combines with the bisulphite of potash to form an isato-sulphite	id. chloro.	
Etc., etc.		

What thinks Wœhler of all this? if not quite so marvellous as his chloro-sulphate of manganese, it is very nearly so.

Let us see what was the reply of Berzelius to my memoir on isatine.

I should first remark, that the discovery of chlorisatine and bichlorisatine was made by Erdmann, who was unacquainted with isatine.

Berzelius in noticing Erdmann's publication, took great pains to show, that the facts therein related, far from according with sub-stitutional ideas, lent a new support to dualism. Then with his usual ability, he pointed out the real arrangement of the atoms in chlorisatine and bichlorisatine.

Dualism was for the third or fourth time unfortunate, for at the same moment that Erdmann published his memoir, I dis-covered isatine, and from it procured directly its chloro and bromo derivatives. I found their composition different from that which had been attributed to them by Erdmann, and his new composition confirmed in an astonishing manner the ideas I had put forth concerning substitutions.

On receiving my memoir, Berzelius took up the ironic vein, he pitied the state of my head, and endeavoured to show, that the chloro-derivatives of isatine, isathyde, &c., were, the one a *sub-porrindinous sub-hypochlorite*, the other a *fulvidinous hypochlorite*, and a third an *acid of rubindene*, &c. One must be blind, said he, not to see this immediately, from simple inspection of the empiric formulæ.

A sub-hypochlorite volatile without decomposition! A sub-hypochlorite undecomposable by sulphuric acid! A sub-hypo-chlorite without action upon vegetable colouring matters! A sub-hypochlorite of an unknown oxide of an unknown porrindene! and all the compounds of isatine treated in the same manner! It is almost incredible.

Worse treated than ever, I published fresh papers on naphtha-line and phenyl, and showed, that chloro and bromo compounds have frequently the same form as the substances from which they were derived.

Hofmann in distilling isatine, chlorisatine, and bichlorisatine, obtained aniline, chloraniline and bichloraniline. He announced that these last, as I had foreseen, possessed the alkaline properties of aniline.

In treating cinchonine with chlorine, I obtained chloro- and bichloro-cinchonine, both of them basic and isomorphous with the primitive alkaloid, and I found that the normal and chloralkaloids deviated the polarised ray in a similar manner. Lastly, I prepared from the sulphate of strichnine, a sulphate of chloro-strichnine, and to two dogs of the same size, I administered respectively an equal dose of each of the two salts. The animals succumbed in the same time, and with the same symptoms of poisoning.

What more could be done to convince the partisans of dualism? Colour, solubility, volatility, vapour density, crystalline form, metamorphoses, action upon polarised light, action upon the animal economy, all testified in favour of the theory of substitutions.

But experiments went for nothing,—dualism had sworn to uphold its position.

Then I associated myself with Gerhardt, for the purpose of defending and propagating our common ideas. Dualism, ashamed of its late defeat, seized upon this occasion to revenge itself. Having at its disposal numerous journals, Scandinavian, German, and French, it let slip no opportunity for attacking me. It aspersed my researches, skilfully avoided the facts that were favorable to my ideas, bantered my style, and ridiculed my person. I was an impostor, the worthy associate of a brigand, &c., &c., and all this for an atom of chlorine put in the place of an atom of hydrogen, for the simple correction of a chemical formula!

I forgive dualism its abuse, but never its dishonesty. Listen to the edifying history thereof.

What reply was made to my last researches? for surely abuse does not constitute argument. To persist in denying the analogy of certain compounds with their chloro-derivatives was no longer possible; so they even seized upon this analogy, which they had all along denied, and used it as a weapon against me. For the third or fourth time they altered the formulæ of isatine and chlorisatine, and then exclaimed, in the tone of victors, "If Laurent's ideas had not been twisted and falsified by his absurd theories, he would have perceived, that the analogy of isatine with chlorisatine, depends upon the *copulæ* which the two bodies contain."

A word let fall from the pen of Gerhardt, was thus transformed into a luminous idea for dualism. From this time everything was copulated. Acetic, formic, butyric, margaric, &c., acids,— alkaloids, ethers, amides, anilides, all became copulated bodies. So that to make acetanilide, for example, they no longer employed acetic acid and aniline, but they re-copulated a copulated oxalic acid with a copulated ammonia. I am inventing nothing—altering nothing. Is it my fault if, while writing history, I appear to be composing a romance?

What then is a copula?

A copula is an imaginary body, the presence of which disguises all the chemical properties of the compounds with which it is united. Thus margaric acid contains oxalic acid united to the copula $C^{32}H^{66}$; and butyric acid, oxalic acid united to the copula C^6H^{14}.

But, it may be asked, what proof is there that margaric and butyric acids contain oxalic acid? It is precisely because there is no proof, that they do contain it. We have just said that copulæ disguise the properties of the bodies to which they are united. If, by any reaction, we could render probable the existence of oxalic acid in margaric acid, this reaction would prove that margaric acid was not a copulated body. Reactions are quite incapable of unravelling the mystery, nought but the penetrating spirit of dualism will suffice.

But admitting that acetic acid is a copulated body, what has that to do with the analogy subsisting between certain bodies and their chloro-derivatives? Let us see. Acetic acid, say these gentlemen, contains oxalic acid, copulated with C^2H^6; trichloracetic acid also contains oxalic acid, but its copula is C^2Cl^6. But by paying regard to the composition of the two acids, we perceive, that the atoms are arranged in the same manner, and that consequently they ought to have analogous properties.

$$(C^2H^6)C^2O^3.H^2O$$
$$(C^2Cl^6)C^2O^3.H^2O$$

The dishonesty is flagrant. What have I to do with your copulæ, your radicals, and your castles of cards? Have I not said over and over again, that I was unacquainted with the arrangement of the atoms in acetic acid? Have I not everywhere repeated, that the chloro-acid must have the same arrangement as the normal acid? Have I not said that the analogy between these two acids was due to this similarity of arrangement? And do you now say otherwise? Only to disguise your defeat, you clothe your formulæ with copulæ, and affect to understand the real arrangement of the atoms. You may possibly be correct in your opinion, but your penetration in this respect appears to me as questionable as your honesty. You have too often varied in your manner of viewing this subject, for me to accept your notions until they are supported by proofs.[21]

Come what may, however, the substitution of chlorine for hydrogen is henceforth an admitted fact.

We shall presently see, that this simple fact materially alters

---

[21] [In spite of Laurent's criticism, the idea of the copula did include a new insight. The substitution of hydrogen by chlorine leads to little change in properties, only if the substitution occurs in a hydrocarbon grouping. Such a grouping was designated a copula by Berzelius. By this admision he retained the dualistic scheme in all areas except hydrocarbon substitutions.—O.T.B.]

the aspect of science, and enables us with ease, to classify, name, and formulate, one half of all organic substances.

Nitrogen Substitutions. Nitrogen, phosphorus, arsenic, and antimony, form a group of equivalent elements, and do not appear to have any analogy with other bodies. We may say, that they do not exercise any action upon organic substances,—that they do not combine directly with them,—and that they do not even displace one another mutually from their combinations. Lastly, they all possess the remarkable property of originating alkaloids.

3

Alexander W. Williamson

On the Constitution of Salts

[From *Chemical Gazette*, *9*, 334–339 (1851). This article was reprinted in the *Journal of the Chemical Society*, *4*, 350–355 (1852).]

There is strong reason for believing that all questions concerning the chemical constitution of matter will be most tangible when considered from the point of view of the constitution of salts, which are the groups whose arrangement and transformations are most susceptible of being ascertained experimentally. The elementary bodies themselves have been now shown[1] to obey a certain force of combination between their particles, analogous though generally inferior to that which holds together the constituents of a salt; and any general conclusions which may be established for salts, will therefore extend to them. Now to have clear and connected notions of any order of phænomena, it is necessary to be able to judge of the various cases belonging to it from the same point of view; or, in other words, to have a uniform standard of comparison. Thus if the value of mechanical forces had to be compared, it would evidently not do to measure the one in pounds and the other in kilogrammes, unless the relative value of these units were known, *i.e.* unless the statement made in the one could be reduced to its equivalent in the other. Such unity has as yet been but little attended to by the majority of chemists; and the different branches of the science remaining disconnected, their efforts were directed to establish details rather than general laws. Thanks to the numerous facts which have been thus established, it is now possible, and even necessary, to do something more. The researches of MM. Laurent and Gerhardt have been mainly directed to this point, and it is well known how fruitful their conclusions have already proved. The following remarks have an intimate connexion with those conclusions, and will hardly be intelligible without a knowledge of them.

We are all agreed that chemistry is concerned with the material

---

[1] See Mr. Brodie's research "On the Condition of certain Elements at the moment of Chemical Change."

process of the transformations and changes which matter undergoes, and that the study of the properties of matter in themselves, as long as they undergo no change, belongs to physics. The chemical formulæ, by which we describe more briefly than by words the transformations supposed known to take place, have as yet answered that purpose very imperfectly, and have presented great irregularity of method; for although generally denoting a certain arrangement of atoms, or at least certain differences of arrangement, they are sometimes used to describe the origin of a compound or its decompositions, without forming any other representation of its actual constitution than what may be contained in such a statement. M. Gerhardt has, in a recent memoir published conjointly with M. Chancel, given considerable development to this latter method; and his so-called synoptic formulæ will, I think, be found very suggestive and useful expressions. But formulæ may be used in an entirely different, and yet perfectly definite manner, and the use of two distinct points of view will perhaps not be unserviceable. They may be used as an actual image of what we rationally suppose to be the arrangement of constituent atoms in a compound, as an orrery is an image of what we conclude to be the arrangement of our planetary system; and decompositions may be actually effected between them by the exchange of a molecule in one group for a molecule in another. Gerhardt's formula for sulphate of soda (if he extends his principles to inorganic chemistry) would be sulphuric acid plus soda minus water. This, no doubt, gives a possible origin of the salt, but by no means a possible decomposition; in other instances the inverse would be the case. But the term sulphate of soda does not mean a body formed in any one particular way; it is equally applicable to the product of the action of sulphuric acid on chloride of sodium, or on carbonate of soda, or even to the product of the action of soda on sulphate of iron. The written name should be made to represent what we conceive a compound *to be*, and should be such that it might be formed by any one of the various processes by which the compound may be prepared. Sulphate of soda is a physical term, and corresponds to purely physical properties; for the substance described by it does not by itself undergo any change, but only when acted upon by certain foreign substances under suitable circumstances.

When we study a molecule by itself, we study it physically; chemistry considers the *change* effected by its reaction upon another molecule, and has to describe the process by which that change is effected. A chemical decomposition should therefore be represented by the juxtaposition of the formulæ of the reacting substances, and

ALEXANDER W. WILLIAMSON (1824–1904).
From the Supplement to *The Illustrated London
News*, September 20, 1873.

by effecting in these formulæ the change which takes place in the mixture.

The adoption of such a method will of course necessitate the adoption of types, from which, by the replacement of certain elements or molecules, we can deduce the constitution of more and more complex groups. I believe that throughout inorganic chemistry, and for the best-known organic compounds, one single type[2] will be found sufficient; it is that of water, represented as containing 2 atoms of hydrogen to 1 of oxygen, thus $\frac{H}{H}O$. In many cases a multiple of this formula must be used, and we shall presently see how we thereby get an explanation of the difference between monobasic and bibasic acids, &c.

I will here give a few examples of the application of this universal type to the formulæ of common substances. The experiments of M. Chancel, agreeing in result with my own, have clearly proved that the numerous family designated as hydrated oxides are not formed by the juxtaposition of an atom of water with an atom of metallic oxide, *e.g.* $K^2O + H^2O$, but that the equivalent of the molecule is half of that quantity, namely $\frac{H}{K}O$; they are not compounds of water, but products of substitution in water.[3] This fact is as applicable to the compound as to the simple radicals; and alcohols, which are truly hydrated oxides, must be considered as products of substitution of the compound radicals, methyle, CH^3 æthyle, C^2H^5; amyle, C^5H^{11}; œnanthyle, C^7H^{15} (Buis), &c. for half the hydrogen of water, $\frac{H}{(CH^3)}O$, $\frac{H}{C^2H^5}O$, &c. The anhydrous oxides of metals

---

[2] [Williamson here proposes the fundamental inorganic type, H_2O, to which Gerhardt later added H_2 and HCl, Wurtz and Hofmann NH_3, Odling and Kekulé CH_4. All organic substances were considered substitution products of these or their multiples.—O.T.B.]

[3] [The major demonstration that alcohols have the formula ROH and ethers R_2O, rather than $R_2O.H_2O$ and R_2O respectively was provided by Williamson himself in his synthesis of mixed ethers ROR' (*Phil. Mag.* [3], *37*, 350–6 (1850)). On the earlier theory, the reagents potassium ethoxide and methyl iodide were written $C^4H^{10}O.K^2O$ and $C^2H^6I^2$ and could only form two separate ethers, $C^4H^{10}O$ and C^2H^6O (+2KI). Instead a mixed ether, methyl ethyl ether, was obtained. This result indicated that alcohol was not a hydrate of ether. Instead, ethers were substitution products of alcohols. If ethyl ether is $C_4H_{10}O$, then ethyl alcohol must be C_2H_5OH and the reaction above is written

$$\frac{C_2H_5}{K}O + C_2H_5I = KI + \frac{C_2H_5}{C_2H_5}O.$$

If chemists had universally accepted Avogadro's hypothesis, the question would not have arisen. Ethyl alcohol having a lower gas density than ether must have a smaller molecular weight; it cannot be the hydrate of the latter.—O.T.B.]

have both atoms of hydrogen replaced by the metal, as $\frac{K}{K}$O, in the same way as common æther, and its homologues have æthyle in place of both the atoms of hydrogen.

In extending this mode of notation to salts and compound æthers, we must of course keep carefully in view the capacity of saturation of their acids, writing the monobasic acids as hydrochloric, nitric, acetic, &c. at half their usual equivalents, ClH, NO^3 H, C^2 H^4 O^2, but retaining the customary atomic weights of the bibasic acids, as sulphuric, carbonic, oxalic, &c.

As alcohol is truly an acid in its reaction, we must of course consider the potassium-alcohol, $\frac{C^2\ H^5}{K}$ O, as its salt, though alkaline in its reactions. We only need to replace 2 atoms of hydrogen in the radical of this salt by oxygen, to have a compound of which the saline character is acknowledged, acetate of potash, $\frac{(C^2\ H^3\ O)}{K}$O. The most simple manner of representing the rational constitution of this compound is to state that it contains, in lieu of the æthyle of the former salt, an oxygen-æthyle, C^2 H^3 O, which we may term othyle. If the 2 atoms of hydrogen in water were replaced by this othyle, we should have anhydrous acetic acid, $\frac{(C^2\ H^3\ O)}{(C^2\ H^3\ O)}$O. In fact, the so-called anhydrous acids[4] are nothing else than the *æthers* of the hydrated acids.

Again, by replacing the potassium in the æthylate, $\frac{C^2\ H^5}{K}$ O, by its equivalent of cyanogen (which may be effected by the action of iodide of cyanogen), we obtain a compound of the composition $\frac{C^2\ H^5}{(NC)}$ O, that is, cyanic æther. It is well known, from Wurtz's elegant researches, that by acting upon this body by hydrate of potash, we obtain carbonate of potash and æthylamine; that is, in the place of carbonic oxide in the cyanate, we get hydrogen, and reciprocally with the hydrate. Now can this exchange be represented more simply than by stating the fact, that, in the following diagram, the hydrogen of the 2 atoms of hydrate of potash changes places with the carbonic oxide of the cyanate:—

$$\begin{matrix} K^2 \\ (H^2) \\ C^2\ H^5 \\ N \end{matrix}\begin{matrix} \\ O^2 \\ \\ (CO) \end{matrix} = \begin{matrix} K^2 \\ CO \\ C^2\ H^5 \\ N \end{matrix}\begin{matrix} \\ O^2 \\ \\ H^2 \end{matrix}$$

---

[4] [Williamson's anhydrous acids are now termed acid anhydrides.—O.T.B.]

1 atom of carbonic oxide is here equivalent to 2 atoms of hydrogen, and by replacing them, holds together the 2 atoms of hydrate in which they were contained, thus necessarily forming a bibasic compound, $\genfrac{}{}{0pt}{}{(CO)}{K^2}O^2$.

If we knew how to form the compound COCl, *i.e.* phosgen, with half as much chlorine, it would be easy, by the reaction of it upon our æthylate of potassium, to prepare oxalic æther (and chloride of potassium). Oxalic æther is therefore alcohol in which the basic hydrogen is replaced by carbonic oxide with twice the equivalent that it possesses in the carbonates; and the best evidence of the truth of this view is afforded by M. Dumas's elegant reaction of ammonia upon the æther, forming the compound of amidogen with carbonic oxide (oxamide), and replacing the carbonic oxide by hydrogen, *reproducing alcohol*:—

$$\left.\begin{array}{l} C^2 H^5 \\ (CO)^2\ O^2 \\ (H^2)\ H^4\ N^2 \end{array}\right\} = 2\left(\begin{array}{l} C^2\ H^5 \\ H \\ (CO)^2\ H^4\ N^2 \end{array} O\right). \quad 5$$

Sulphurous acid is another radical capable of replacing hydrogen; and the sulphates are thus reduced to our type, being bibasic from the same reason as the carbonates. We have thus for sulphuric acid, $\genfrac{}{}{0pt}{}{SO^2}{H^2}O^2$; acid sulphate of potash, $\genfrac{}{}{0pt}{}{SO^2}{HK}O^2$; neutral sulphate, $\genfrac{}{}{0pt}{}{SO^2}{K^2}O^2$, &c.

There are various reactions, both of formation and decomposition, of sulphates, which bear out this view; for instance, chlorosulphuric acid, SO^2Cl^2, in contact with 2 atoms of water, at once replaces half the hydrogen in both by SO^2, forming 2(ClH) and $\genfrac{}{}{0pt}{}{SO^2}{H^2}O^2$. And again, the difference of the action of zinc upon sulphuric acid according to the concentration, evolving at one time hydrogen, at another sulphurous acid, affords evidence that the sulphurous acid is contained in a manner similar to the hydrogen.

Nitric acid presents, according to the usual view of its constitution, a singular difference between its behaviour to organic and to inorganic compounds; but this difference is owing merely to the error of that view. We are taught that nitric acid combines

---

5 [The first C^2H^5 should read $(C^2H^5)^2$. In modern form this equation would read:

$$\begin{array}{l} COOC_2H_5 \\ | \qquad\qquad + 2NH_3 \rightarrow \\ COOC_2H_5 \end{array} \quad \begin{array}{l} CONH_2 + 2C_2H_5OH. \\ | \\ CONH_2 \end{array}$$

—O.T.B.]

directly with mineral bases; but when reacting upon hydrogen compounds, it has a powerful tendency to replace hydrogen by hyponitric acid. Now if hydrogen, in organic compounds without number, be replaceable by hyponitric acid, why should not also the hydrogen in hydrate of potash be so replaceable? The product of that substitution would be no very improbable body, only common nitrate of potash, $\genfrac{}{}{0pt}{}{(NO^2)}{K} O^2$.

One more example, and I have done. Chlorine is well known to react upon hydrogen compounds by replacing hydrogen by chlorine, with formation of hydrochloric acid. So it is also when it reacts upon water in presence of bases, $\genfrac{}{}{0pt}{}{Cl}{H} O$ (hydrated hypochlorous acid), and ClH being formed. In like manner we have, for the series of oxygen acids of this radical, the formulæ $\genfrac{}{}{0pt}{}{(ClO)}{H} O$, chlorous acid; $\genfrac{}{}{0pt}{}{(ClO^2)}{H} O$, chloric acid; $\genfrac{}{}{0pt}{}{(ClO^3)}{H} O$, perchloric acid.

In order to accomplish what I above alluded to as a desideratum for the explanation of chemical reactions, namely effecting between the formulæ of the reagents the interchange supposed to take place in the mixture, I have fixed the symbols of those atoms which have to change places upon the extremities of a piece of card, so fixed by a pivot to the board that by turning round 180° it reverses the positions of the exchanging atoms.

I would not have brought before the public considerations so purely theoretical as the above, had I not found the conclusions of considerable practical utility in the study of reactions.

In the theory of types, we owe to M. Dumas an idea which has already been the vehicle of many an important discovery in science, and which is undoubtedly destined to receive still more general application.

To prevent misunderstandings, it may be as well to state, that the radicals which I have here so freely used are not supposed to be in their compounds absolutely the same as in the free state. The same remark applies with equal force to metallic bodies, which on entering into combination give off a certain amount of heat, and thus assume different properties. To say that metallic zinc is contained in its sulphate is an expression authorized by usage, but is only strictly true by abstraction from most of the properties of the metal. The material atom, which under certain circumstances possesses the properties which we describe by the word "zinc," is no doubt contained in the sulphate, but with different properties, and in the chloride with properties different from either; so also of the compound radicals.

It is to be hoped that we may soon be able to give an account of the nature of the processes by which these changes of properties are effected; but that task can only be entered upon when we have obtained exact determinations of the relative momentum of atoms in various compounds, the proportion of which to their masses determines their physical and chemical properties.

4

Edward Frankland

On a New Series of Organic Bodies Containing Metals[1]

[From *Philosophical Transactions of the Royal Society of London*, *142*, 417–444 (1852).]

Under the above title I described, more than three years ago, some preliminary experiments[2] which proved the existence of certain organic compounds highly analogous to cacodyl, and, like that body, consisting of a metal, or in some cases phosphorus, associated with the groups C_2H_3, C_4H_5, C_6H_7, &c.,[3] and possessing, in most instances, highly remarkable powers of combination. I fixed the composition and studied some of the reactions of two of these bodies, to which the names Zincmethyl (C_2H_3Zn) and Zincethyl (C_4H_5Zn) were provisionally assigned, besides giving methods for procuring similar compounds containing tin, arsenic and phosphorus, by acting upon the iodides of the alcohol radicals with these elements, and expressing a belief, founded upon the similarity of functions existing between hydrogen and the groups of the form $C_nH_{(n+1)}$,

---

[1] [Frankland had come across organometallic compounds quite accidentally. As a student of Kolbe's, he had become interested in the production of free radicals, considering them the organic equivalents of metals. He used the usual displacement procedure

$$Zn + 2C_2H_5I \rightarrow ZnI_2 + \text{"ethyl"}$$

and assumed that the resulting gas was free ethyl. It was later realized that he had actually prepared butane, C_4H_{10}. Free ethyl was finally prepared by Paneth in 1929 by an essentially analogous reaction (F. Paneth and W. Hofeditz, *Ber.*, *62B*, 1335 (1929)). The detection method, however, had to be greatly refined, the half-life of ethyl radicals being of the order of a thousandth of a second at room temperature.

During Frankland's experiment a white crystalline compound was deposited. Investigation of this ethyl zinc iodide led to his systematic study of organometallic compounds.

The section dealing directly with the valence concept appears on pp. 104 ff. —O.T.B.]

[2] Annalen der Chemie und Pharmacie, Bd. LXXI. s. 213, and Journal of the Chemical Society, vol. ii. p. 297.

[3] [Frankland is using C=6 here. The radicals would now read CH_3, C_2H_5, C_3H_7.—O.T.B.]

EDWARD FRANKLAND (1825–1899). From
Famous Chemists, The Men and Their Work by Sir
William A. Tilden. London: George Routledge
& Sons, Ltd.; New York: E. P. Dutton & Co., 1921.

that most, if not the whole, of the compounds contained in the following series might be formed; those marked thus * being at that time already known.

Hydrogen series.	Methyl series.	Ethyl series.	Butyl series.[4]	Valyl series.[4]	Amyl series.	Phenyl series.
ZnH	Zn C_2H_3*	Zn C_4H_5*	Zn C_6H_7	Zn C_8H_9	Zn $C_{10}H_{11}$	Zn $C_{12}H_5$
AsH_3*	As$(C_2H_3)_2$*	As$(C_4H_5)_2$	As$(C_6H_7)_2$	As$(C_8H_9)_2$	As$(C_{10}H_{11})_2$	As$(C_{12}H_5)_2$
SbH_3*	Sb$(C_2H_3)_3$	Sb$(C_4H_5)_3$	Sb$(C_6H_7)_3$	Sb$(C_8H_9)_3$	Sb$(C_{10}H_{11})_3$	Sb$(C_{12}H_5)_3$
P H_3*	P $(C_2H_3)_3$*	P $(C_4H_5)_3$	P $(C_6H_7)_3$	P $(C_8H_9)_3$	P $(C_{10}H_{11})_3$	P $(C_{12}H_5)_3$

More recently Löwig and Schweitzer[5] have commenced labouring in the same field, and have filled up one of the gaps in the foregoing table by the formation of stibethyl ($Sb(C_4H_5)_3$), in acting upon iodide of ethyl with an alloy of antimony and potassium; the same chemists state also the probable formation of similar compounds containing methyl and amyl in place of ethyl, and bismuth and phosphorus instead of antimony.

I have continued my researches upon the organo-metallic bodies formed as above described, and having succeeded in increasing the list by the addition of several new members, I propose, in a series of papers, of which this is the first, to lay before the Royal Society the results of my experiments on the formation of bodies of this class.

The agents which I have hitherto employed in the formation of these organo-metallic compounds are two, viz. heat and light; in many cases either of these can be used, in others only one can be made to effect the desired combination, whilst more rarely the assistance of both appears to be essential. In those experiments in which heat was employed the materials were subjected to its action in sealed glass tubes, about 12 inches long, and varying in diameter from half an inch to 1 inch, the thickness of the glass being about one-eighth of an inch.[6] To preserve the gaseous products of the operation in a state of perfect purity for subsequent investigation, the tubes were well exhausted before being sealed; they were then immersed to about half their depth in an oil-bath, and heated to the required temperature. In cases where the influence of light was employed, the materials, confined in tubes of precisely similar dimensions, were exposed to the sun's rays, concentrated in most cases by an 18-inch parabolic reflector, near the focus of which the

---

[4] [The butyl series is our propyl series C_3H_7; the valyl series is our butyl series C_4H_9.—O.T.B.]

[5] Annalen der Chemie und Pharmacie, Bd. LXXV. s. 315.

[6] A minute account of the construction and use of these tubes is given in the Journal of the Chemical Society, vol. ii. p. 265.

tubes were placed, either naked or surrounded by a solution of sulphate of copper to absorb the calorific rays. By this arrangement the light and heat could be increased, diminished or modified at pleasure, which was found very convenient in several of the operations.

Action of Tin upon Iodide of Ethyl. When iodide of ethyl and metallic tin are exposed to the action of either heat or light, the tin gradually dissolves in the ethereal liquid, which finally solidifies to a mass of nearly colourless crystals. This reaction is effected most conveniently by the action of light, an excess of tinfoil, cut into narrow slips, being employed: the sealed tubes containing these ingredients should be placed near the focus of a large parabolic reflector, the temperature being prevented, if necessary, from rising too high by immersing them in water or in a solution of sulphate of copper. The unconcentrated rays of the sun, or even diffused daylight, are quite sufficient to determine the formation of the crystalline body; but an exposure of several weeks, or even months, would be necessary for the completion of the change, which is effected by the use of the reflector in a few days of bright sunshine. The liquid gradually assumes a straw-yellow colour, but its solidification is prevented as long as possible at the end of the operation, by allowing the temperature to rise 20° or 30° C. above that of the atmosphere; thus nearly the whole of the iodide of ethyl becomes united with tin. When heat instead of light is employed to effect the combination, the tubes should not be more than half an inch in diameter, and to avoid the risk of explosion, should not be more than one-fourth filled with the materials: the combination takes place at about 180° C. The agency of heat is therefore much less convenient than that of light in the production of this reaction, which is also never so complete as when the latter agent is employed; I have satisfied myself, however, that the results are the same in both cases.

Examination of Solid Products. The capillary extremities of the tubes in which the iodide of ethyl had been exposed to the action of tin were broken off under sulphuretted water and beneath a jar filled with the same liquid;[7] the gases evolved were preserved for eudiometrical investigation. The crystalline product of the reaction was then withdrawn from the tubes, and after being exposed to

---

[7] Journal of Chemical Society, vol. ii. p. 267.

a gentle heat for a few minutes to expel the iodide of ethyl that had escaped combination, was treated with alcohol, in which the crystals readily dissolved, leaving only a small residue of a bright red colour, which proved to be protoiodide of tin. The filtered alcoholic solution was then placed over sulphuric acid *in vacuo*, where it soon deposited a large crop of long needle-like crystals, which, when freed from the mother-liquor, washed with a small quantity of dilute alcohol, dried between folds of bibulous paper, and finally over sulphuric acid *in vacuo*, yielded the following analytical results:—

I. 1·6806 grm., treated with aqueous solution of ammonia, was immediately decomposed, iodide of ammonium being formed, whilst the iodine in the original compound became, as I shall show below, replaced by oxygen; this oxide, which is almost absolutely insoluble in ammonia, collected on a filter and dried at 100° C., weighed ·7263 grm.; decomposed by boiling nitric acid it gave ·5811 grm. peroxide of tin. The ammoniacal solution, acidulated with nitric acid and precipitated by nitrate of silver, yielded 1·8418 grm. iodide of silver. After precipitation of the excess of nitrate of silver by hydrochloric acid, sulphuretted hydrogen was passed through the solution, and the slight precipitate formed was washed, dried, ignited and added to the above peroxide of tin, in the weight of which it is included.

II. 1·4254 grm., burnt with oxide of copper, 2 inches of metallic copper being placed in front of the combustion-tube, gave ·5858 grm. carbonic acid and ·2975 grm. water.

III. 1·2209 grm. gave 0·5008 grm. carbonic acid and ·2580 grm. water.

IV. 2·0980 grms., treated as described in No. I., yielded ·9218 grm. of the body produced by the action of solution of ammonia, which yielded ·7239 grm. peroxide of tin. The ammoniacal solution, precipitated by nitrate of silver as in No. I., produced 2·2883 grms. iodide of silver.

V. ·9113 grm. gave ·3735 grm. carbonic acid and ·1908 grm. water.[8]

These numbers show that the crystalline body is a compound of one atom of ethyl, one atom of tin, and one atom of iodine. The formula—

$$C_4H_5SnI$$

requires the following values:—

---

[8] The substance used in Nos. IV. and V. was produced by the action of light, that used in the other analyses by the agency of heat.

		Calculated.		Found.[9]			
				I.	II.	III.	IV.	V.
C_4	.	24	11·18	——	11·21	11·19	——	11·18
H_5	.	5	2·33	——	2·32	2·35	——	2·33
Sn	.	58·82	27·40	27·18	——	——	27·12	
I	. .	126·84	59·09	59·21	——	——	58·76	
			100·00					

For reasons described below, I propose to call this compound *iodide of stanethylium.*

Iodide of stanethylium crystallizes in transparent, slightly straw-coloured needles, which are right reactangular prisms, frequently one-twelfth of an inch broad and 2 or 3 inches in length. They are very soluble in ether and in boiling alcohol; less so in cold alcohol and in water; the watery solution is decomposed on boiling, oxide of stanethylium being precipitated and hydriodic acid formed. Iodide of stanethylium fuses at 42° C., and boils at 240° C., undergoing at the same time partial decomposition: it possesses, at common temperatures, a peculiar pungent odour, somewhat resembling the volatile oil of mustard, and which irritates the eyes and lining membrane of the nose, causing a discharge which continues for several hours or even days, especially if the vapour from the heated iodide of stanethylium be inhaled; yet this compound can scarcely be said to be volatile at common temperatures, since a few grains may be exposed to the air for several weeks without any appreciable loss of weight.

Oxide of Stanethylium. In contact with solutions of the alkalies, iodide of stanethylium is immediately decomposed, oxide of stanethylium and an alkaline iodide being formed; with solutions of potash and soda the oxide of stanethylium dissolves in an excess of the precipitant, but is reprecipitated, unchanged, by cautious neutralization of the alkaline solution; with solution of ammonia the precipitated oxide remains undissolved on the addition of an excess of the alkali; a quantity of the oxide of stanethylium, prepared in this latter manner, was heated for a few minutes with an excess of ammonia, thrown on a filter and washed with distilled water until all iodide of ammonium was removed. Submitted to analysis it yielded the following results:—

---

[9] [Frankland is using C=6, H=1, O=8, Sn=58.82, I=126.84, corresponding approximately to the first system described by Odling (see above, p. 41), the system of equivalents developed by Gmelin.—O.T.B.]

I. ·3497 grm., burnt with oxide of copper, gave ·3218 grm. carbonic acid and ·1630 grm. water.

II. ·7296 grm., decomposed by nitric acid and ignited, gave ·5778 grm. peroxide of tin.

III. ·9218 grm. gave, when similarly treated, ·7239 grm. peroxide of tin. These numbers agree closely with the formula—

$$C_4H_5SnO,$$

as is seen by the following comparison:—

		Calculated.		| Found.		
				I.	II.	III.
C_4	. 24	25·05		25·09	——	——
H_5	. 5	5·22		5·18	——	——
Sn	. 58·82	61·39		——	62·25	61·73
O .	. 8	8·34		——	——	——
		100·00				

Analyses Nos. I. and IV. of iodide of stanethylium also clearly show the transformation of the iodide into the oxide of stanethylium by ammonia; in analysis No. I. 1·6806 grm. of iodide of stanethylium gave ·7263 grm. of oxide of stanethylium, and in analysis No. IV. 2·0980 grms. of the iodide yielded ·9218 grm. of the oxide of stanethylium. Hence

	Calculated.	| Found.	
		I.	II.
100 parts of iodide of stanethylium } yield of oxide of stanethylium	44·64	43·22	43·93

The numbers obtained by experiment correspond sufficiently well with the theoretical one, when it is considered that oxide of stanethylium is not absolutely insoluble in excess of ammonia.

Oxide of stanethylium presents the appearance of a somewhat cream-white amorphous powder, closely resembling peroxide of tin, but less heavy than that oxide; it has a peculiar though slight ethereal odour and a bitter taste; it is insoluble in water, alcohol and ether, but readily dissolves in solutions of acids and of the fixed alkalies; with acids it forms salts, which are, however, for the most part difficultly crystallizable; those with strong acids exhibit an acid reaction. The nitrate deflagrates when heated to about 120° C., and on the application of a higher heat becomes pure peroxide of tin. The salts of oxide of stanethylium behave with reagents so nearly like the salts of peroxide of tin, that the two are very difficult to distinguish from each other.

Sulphide of Stanethylium. When sulphuretted hydrogen is passed through an acid solution of a salt of stanethylium, a cream-coloured precipitate falls, which is insoluble in dilute acids and ammonia, but soluble in concentrated hydrochloric acid, solutions of the fixed alkalies, and alkaline sulphides; from its solutions in the fixed alkalies and alkaline sulphides, it is reprecipitated, unchanged, on the addition of an acid. I have made no analyses of this body, but there is no doubt that its formula is—

$$C_4H_5SnS,$$

and that it is produced by the following reaction—

$$C_4H_5SnO + HS = C_4H_5SnS + HO.$$

Sulphide of stanethylium presents the appearance of an amorphous cream-coloured powder, having a pungent and very nauseous smell, resembling decayed horse-radish: when heated it fuses, froths up and decomposes, emitting vapours of a most insupportable odour. Heated with nitric acid it is decomposed with the formation of peroxide of tin.

Chloride of Stanethylium. C_4H_5SnCl. This salt is best prepared by dissolving oxide of stanethylium in dilute hydrochloric acid: on evaporation at a gentle heat or over sulphuric acid *in vacuo*, the chloride crystallizes out in long colourless needles, isomorphous with the iodide, which salt it also closely resembles in all its properties; it is however more volatile, and therefore emits a more intensely pungent and irritating odour than the iodide.

Stanethylium. When a strip of zinc is immersed in a solution of a salt of stanethylium (a solution of the chloride of stanethylium is the best for this purpose), it speedily becomes covered with dense oily drops of a yellow colour, which finally separate from the lower extremity of the zinc and accumulate at the bottom of the vessel; the formation of the oily liquid is much favoured by the application of a gentle heat. The yellow oil was separated from the supernatant liquid by means of a pipette, and well washed with successive large portions of cold water; being then dried over chloride of calcium and submitted to analysis, it yielded the following results:—

I. ·3150 grm., burnt with oxide of copper and oxygen gas, gave ·3498 grm. carbonic acid and ·1757 grm. water.

These numbers correspond sufficiently with the formula

$$C_4H_5Sn,$$

when it is considered that the stanethylium, as thus prepared, contains traces of undecomposed chloride of stanethylium, which I did not succeed in removing by the most protracted washing; and as stanethylium does not crystallize and cannot be distilled without decomposition, I could not avail myself of these means of purification. The above formula requires the following numbers:—

						Calculated.	Found.
C_4	.	.	.	.	24	27·32	26·95
H_5	.	.	.	.	5	5·69	5·51
Sn	.	.	.	.	58·82	66·99	——
						100·00	

The isolation of stanethylium from its chloride by zinc, is therefore expressed by the following simple equation:—

$$\left.\begin{matrix} C_4H_5SnCl \\ Zn \end{matrix}\right\} = \left\{\begin{matrix} ZnCl \\ C_4H_5Sn. \end{matrix}\right.$$

Stanethylium exists at the ordinary atmospheric temperature, as a thick, heavy, oily liquid, of a yellow or brownish-yellow colour, and an exceedingly pungent odour, resembling that of its compounds, but much more powerful. It is insoluble in water, but soluble in alcohol and ether. At about 150° C. it enters into ebullition, a quantity of metallic tin is deposited, and a colourless liquid distils over, having a peculiar odour, containing a considerable quantity of tin, and exhibiting no tendency to combine with iodine or bromine: the composition and properties of this liquid I have not further ascertained; it possibly consists of or contains *binethide of tin* $(Sn(C_4H_5)_2)$. In contact with the air stanethylium rapidly attracts oxygen and is converted into a white powder, which has all the properties of oxide of stanethylium. Chloride, bromide and iodide of stanethylium are immediately formed by the action of chlorine, bromine and iodine, or their hydrogen acids respectively, upon stanethylium; the first and third are in every respect identical with the salts above described. I have analytically examined the bromide prepared by adding an alcoholic solution of bromine to an alcoholic solution of stanethylium until the colour of the bromine no longer disappears; by spontaneous evaporation the bromide of stanethylium is deposited in long white needles, which closely resemble, both in appearance and properties, the chloride of stanethylium. These crystals, pressed between folds of bibulous paper, and dried over sulphuric acid *in vacuo*, gave the following analytical results:—

·9730 grm., burnt with oxide of copper, yielded ·5108 grm. carbonic acid and ·2582 grm. water.

These numbers agree very closely with the formula—

$$C_4H_5SnBr,$$

as is seen from the following comparison:—

	Equivs.		Calculated.	Found.
Carbon . .	4	24	14·30	14·32
Hydrogen . .	5	5	2·98	2·95
Tin	1	58·82	35·05	——
Bromine . .	1	80·00	47·67	——
		167·82	100·00	

These results show that stanethylium perfectly resembles cacodyl[10] in its reactions, combining directly with the electro-negative elements and regenerating the compounds from which it has been derived.

Examination of Gases. The examination of the gases evolved on opening the tubes in which iodide of ethyl and tin had been submitted to the action of heat, and which were allowed to stand over sulphuretted water for twelve hours, yielded the following results. Specific gravity:—

Weight of flask filled with gas . . .	35·4712 grms.
Temperature of room	20·8° C.
Height of barometer	761·2 mm.
Height of internal column of mercury .	15·2 mm.
Temperature in balance case	22·6° C.
Weight of flask filled with dry air . .	35·4703 grms.
Temperature in balance case	22·8° C.
Capacity of flask	140·50 cubic centimetres.

From these data the specific gravity was calculated to be 1·0384. The remainder of the gas was submitted to eudiometrical

---

[10] [Cacodyl, prepared originally by Bunsen, was claimed by him to be a free radical. The formula of the radical would be $As(CH_3)_2$. He had actually prepared $(CH_3)_2AsAs(CH_3)_2$. Cacodyl is discussed again on p. 102 where Frankland concludes that it is a compound rather than a radical, though he does not modify its formula.—O.T.B.]

analysis: the following numbers were obtained:—

I. In Short Eudiometer.

	Observed volume.	Temp.	Difference of mercury level.	Barom.	Corrected vol. at 0° C. and 1 metre press.
			mm	mm	
Volume of gas used (dry)	143·4	21·0° C.	16·3	760·5	99·09
Volume after action of fuming SO₃ (dry) . .	122·5	18·2	37·0	754·7	82·42

II. In Combustion Eudiometer.

Volume of gas used (moist)	110·3	18·1 C.	570·7	755·2	17·48
Volume after admission of O (moist) . . .	383·6	18·3	274·7	755·7	167·31
Volume after explosion (moist)	326·9	18·4	332·4	755·8	124·86
Volume after absorption of CO₂ (dry) . . .	264·5	17·0	398·3	760·7	90·23
Volume after admission of H (dry)	592·5	17·0	77·9	761·6	381·33
Volume after explosion (moist)	303·5	17·7	355·9	762·7	111·64

As the gas, left unabsorbed by fuming sulphuric acid, was soluble in about its own volume of alcohol, with the exception of a very small per-centage due to the nitrogen introduced by diffusion through the sulphuretted water, it could not contain either hydrogen or hydride of methyl; and the result of the above combustion proves that it is hydride of ethyl, for I have shown that 1 vol. of hydride of ethyl consumes 3·5 vols. oxygen, and generates 2 vols. carbonic acid, numbers which almost exactly correspond with those obtained.

17·48 vols. of the gas, containing 17·15 vols. of combustible gas and ·33 vol. of nitrogen, consumed 59·93 vols. oxygen and generated 34·63 vols. carbonic acid; hence

Volume of combustible gas.		Oxygen consumed.		Carbonic acid generated.
17·15		59·93		34·63
1	:	3·49	:	2·01

Further, the gas agrees in all its chemical and physical properties, with the hydride of ethyl prepared by the action of zinc upon iodide of ethyl in presence of water.

The composition of the gas absorbed by fuming sulphuric acid was determined by exploding a known volume of the original gas with excess of oxygen, and determining the quantities of oxygen consumed, and carbonic acid generated.

This determination gave the following numbers:—

III.

	Observed volume.	Temp.	Difference of mercury level.	Barom.	Corrected vol. at 0° C. and 1 metre press.
			mm	mm	
Volume of gas used (moist)	122·0	19·7° C.	563·0	764·2	20·95
Volume after admission of O (moist)	424·5	20·0	240·4	764·3	200·33
Volume after explosion (moist)	363·5	20·4	301·0	763·5	150·40
Volume after absorption of CO₂ (dry) . . .	296·7	19·7	366·4	760·4	109·03
Volume after admission of H (dry)	683·1	21·7	4·0	760·8	478·89
Volume after explosion (moist)	368·6	21·8	293·3	761·2	153·09

Hence 20.95 vols. containing 20·62 vols. combustible gas, consumed 70·78 vols. oxygen, and generated 41·37 vols. carbonic acid: now as 20·62 vols. of this gas must contain, according to analyses Nos. I. and II., 17·10 vols. hydride of ethyl, which would consume 59·85 vols. oxygen and generate 34·20 vols. carbonic acid, it is evident that the volumes of oxygen consumed, and carbonic acid generated, by the gas absorbed by fuming sulphuric acid, must bear the following relation to each other:—

Volume of gas absorbable by fuming SO₃.		Oxygen consumed.		Carbonic acid generated.
3·52		10·93		7·17
1	:	3·10	:	2·03

The body removed by fuming sulphuric acid is therefore olefiant gas, 1 vol. of which consumes 3 vols. oxygen, and generates 2 vols. carbonic acid, numbers which correspond sufficiently with those obtained in the above determination.

The last analysis can also be employed to control Nos. I. and II.; for if we represent the volume of nitrogen, contained in the original gas, by x, that of hydride of ethyl by y, and that of olefiant gas by z; and further, the volume of mixed gases, oxygen consumed, and carbonic acid generated, respectively by A, B and C, we have the following equations:—

$$x + y + z = A$$
$$\frac{7}{2}y + 3z = B$$
$$2y + 2z = C,$$

from which the following values for x, y and z are derived:—

$$x = \cdot27$$
$$y = 17\cdot06$$
$$z = 3\cdot62$$

_____

$$20\cdot95$$

The per-centage composition of the gases evolved by the action of heat upon iodide of ethyl and tin is therefore the following:—

	I. and II.	III.
Hydride of ethyl	81·61	81·43
Olefiant gas	16·82	17·28
Nitrogen	1·57	1·29
	_____	_____
	100·00	100·00

This result is also confirmed by the determination of the specific gravity of the gaseous mixture, as is seen from the following calculation:—

C_4H_5H	$81\cdot61 \times 1\cdot03652 =$	$84\cdot590$
C_4H_4	$16\cdot82 \times \cdot96742 =$	$16\cdot272$
N	$1\cdot57 \times \cdot96740 =$	$1\cdot519$

_____

$$\frac{102\cdot381}{100} = 1\cdot02381$$

$$100\cdot00$$

Specific gravity found by experiment . . $= 1\cdot0384$

The presence of hydride of ethyl and olefiant gas amongst the products of the action of heat upon iodide of ethyl and tin, shows that the combination of tin with iodide of ethyl is not the only reaction which takes place, but that a portion of the iodide of ethyl is also decomposed by the tin, with the production of iodide of tin and ethyl; the latter body being transformed at the moment of its liberation into hydride of ethyl and olefiant gas, a catalysis to which this radical is so prone,

$$\left. \begin{array}{c} 2C_4H_5I \\ 2Sn \end{array} \right\} = \left\{ \begin{array}{l} C_4H_5,H \\ C_4H_4 \\ 2Sn\ I \end{array} \right.$$

It was ascertained that protoiodide of tin was present amongst the solid products of the reaction.

The large excess of hydride of ethyl exhibited in the above analysis, may have been caused, either by the greater solubility of olefiant gas in iodide of ethyl (a further and considerable amount of gas being expelled from the tube by the application of a gentle heat), or by the presence of moisture in the materials, which would give rise to the formation of oxyiodide of tin and hydride of ethyl,

$$\left.\begin{array}{r}C_4H_5I \\ HO \\ 2Sn\end{array}\right\} = \left\{\begin{array}{l}C_4H_5H \\ SnO + SnI.\end{array}\right.$$

Both these causes probably contribute to produce the excess of hydride of ethyl; but the very small amount of gaseous products, compared with the solid ones, convinced me that the production of the former is only an accidental circumstance, which, however it may be interpreted, does not at all affect the principal reaction, viz. the formation of iodide of stanethylium. The gases, evolved by the action of light upon iodide of ethyl and tin, are perfectly similar to those obtained by the action of heat.

Stanmethylium and stanamylium are formed when the iodides of methyl and amyl respectively are exposed to the action of light in contact with tin; their salts are isomorphous with those of stanethylium; but I have not yet completed the investigation of these bodies.

Action of Zinc upon Iodide of Methyl. When iodide of methyl and zinc are exposed to a temperature of about 150° C. in a sealed tube, the zinc gradually dissolves with the evolution of gas, whilst a mass of white crystals and a colourless mobile liquid, refracting light strongly, occupy, after a few hours, the place of the original materials. The gas, evolved on breaking off the capillary extremity of the previously exhausted decomposition tube, was collected and preserved over sulphuretted water in the manner already described: I will refer to this gas again under the name of α. On cutting off the upper portion of the decomposition tube and pouring cold distilled water upon the mobile liquid and white mass of crystals just mentioned, a very violent action ensued, and a column of flame several feet high shot up momentarily from the mouth of the tube; but the action soon became more moderate, and a cork and gas-delivering tube being fitted into the decomposition tube, the gas, after all atmospheric air had been expelled, was collected and preserved in an apparatus similar to that used for the gas α. I will call this second gas β.

Zincmethylium. From a preliminary experiment, it was ascertained that the gas evolved on opening the decomposition tube possessed, before contact with water, a most insupportable and very peculiar odour, and that, when ignited or brought in contact with pure oxygen gas, it burnt with a greenish blue flame, producing dense white fumes: when a porcelain plate was held in this flame, it immediately became coated with a jet black deposit, surrounded by a white ring; this black deposit dissolved in dilute hydrochloric acid with evolution of hydrogen gas, and the solution was found to contain chloride of zinc. Hence it was evident that a volatile or gaseous compound of zinc was present amongst the products of decomposition, and this was soon found to reside in the mobile liquid above mentioned; for on inverting the tube and allowing a few drops of the liquid to escape, it inflamed spontaneously the instant it came in contact with the air, and produced, by its combustion, large quantities of oxide of zinc. In order to obtain this liquid in a state of purity, another tube was charged with iodide of methyl and excess of zinc, and subjected to a heat of 150° or 160° C. until every trace of iodide of methyl was decomposed. The drawn out extremity of the tube being broken off, the included gas was allowed to escape, and the liquid contents were then separated from the solid ones by distillation at a gentle heat, in an atmosphere of dry hydrogen. This was accomplished as shown in the following figure.

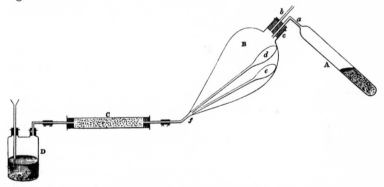

A is the decomposition tube bent at an obtuse angle at *a*, and connected with the receiver B by the doubly perforated cork *c*, which also contains the small tube *b*, open at both ends. The receiver B is drawn out at *f* until its internal diameter is diminished to about $\frac{1}{20}$th of an inch, and this drawn out extremity is connected, by means of a caoutchouc joint, with the chloride of calcium tube C, which at its opposite extremity is in connection with a hydrogen gas apparatus D. *d, e* are two small glass bulbs for preserving the condensed liquid. The apparatus being thus arranged, hydrogen is evolved in D, and becoming perfectly desiccated in passing through the chloride of calcium tube C, enters the receiver B at *f*, expelling the atmospheric air through the tube *b*. When the gas has thus streamed through the apparatus for at least a quarter of an hour, and every trace of air has been expelled from B and from the bulbs *d, e* by diffusion, the extremity of the tube *b* is hermetically sealed, at the same moment that the evolution of gas from D is interrupted. The drawn out extremity of the receiver B being then quickly sealed at *f*; B, *d* and *e* remain filled with pure dry hydrogen, and A with a mixture of gases free from oxygen, as any trace of this element, which might have penetrated there, would be instantaneously absorbed by its contents. B is then immersed to its neck in cold water, and a gentle heat cautiously applied to the whole length of A by means of a spirit lamp. The mobile fluid in A soon enters into ebullition, and distils over into the receiver B; as soon as the distillation is finished and A become cold, its capillary extremity is fused off at *a* by means of a blowpipe, *a* remaining hermetically sealed. The receiver B is then removed from the water and dried; heat is applied to the side adjacent to the bulbs *d, e*, so as to expel a portion of the enclosed gas from their open ends at *f*; on subsequent cooling, a certain quantity of the liquid rises into these bulbs, which are alternately heated and cooled, until every trace of the liquid has not only entered them but passed entirely into their expanded portion, so as to leave the capillary limbs filled with hydrogen. It is of importance that the whole of the liquid should be forced to enter these bulbs, otherwise, on subsequently opening the mouth of the receiver, it inflames, causing the expulsion of the liquid from the bulbs, and thus rendering the experiment abortive. The cork *c* is then removed, and the bulbs *d, e* extracted as quickly as possible, the open capillary extremities being immediately sealed before the blowpipe. The bulbs, having been previously weighed, the increase denotes the weight of the included liquid. The residue in A was found scarcely to effervesce with water, and consisted of iodide of zinc mixed with the excess of metallic zinc employed.

I have fixed the composition of the liquid obtained as above described, and proved it to be a compound of one atom of zinc and and one atom of methyl, by the following experiments:—

I. One of the bulbs above mentioned was opened beneath an inverted receiver filled with recently boiled distilled water; its contents were rapidly resolved into hydrated oxide of zinc and a permanent gas, which last was submitted to eudiometrical examination; the following results were obtained:—

The action of fuming sulphuric acid did not produce any diminution of volume.

The gas was nearly insoluble in absolute alcohol.

A eudiometrical combustion yielded the following results:—

	Observed volume.	Temp.	Difference of mercury level.	Barom.	Corrected vol. at 0° C. and 1 metre press.
			mm	mm	
Volume of gas used (moist)	122·5	18·7° C.	602·2	747·8	14·86
Volume ofter admission of O (moist)	287·9	18·7	418·4	747·6	84·39
Volume after explosion (moist)	232·1	18·6	479·7	747.·4	54·71
Volume after absorption of CO₂ (dry) . . .	188·2	18·6	519·4	747·5	40·19
Voume after admission of H (dry)	549·4	18·4	162·7	747·6	301·04
Volume after explosion (moist)	425·7	18·4	279·0	747·6	180·62

Volume of comb. gas.		Oxygen consumed.		CO₂ generated.
14·86		29·39		14·52
1	:	1·98	:	·98

In order to ascertain whether the gas was a single compound or a gaseous mixture, and also to determine its specific gravity, it was submitted to diffusion in an apparatus which I have already described:[11] the following results were obtained:—

I. In Diffusion Eudiometer.

	Observed volume.	Temp.	Difference of mercury level.	Barom.	Corrected vol. at 0° C. and 1 metre press.
			mm	mm	
Volume of gas used (dry)	173·0	19·0° C.	20·1	741·1	116·61
Volume after diffusion (dry)	144·3	19·2	46·3	740·8	93·63

II. Estimation of Oxygen in residual gas.

	Observed volume.	Temp.	Difference of mercury level.	Barom.	Corrected vol. at 0° C. and 1 metre press.
Volume of gas used (moist)	117·5	19·3	53·1	740·6	75·44
Volume after absorption of O (dry)	101·2	17·0	69·3	742·8	64·16

---

[11] Quarterly Journal of Chemical Society, vol. ii. p. 283.

III. Combustion of Gas remaining after absorption of Oxygen.

	Observed volume.	Temp.	Difference of mercury level.	Barom.	Corrected vol. at 0° C. and 1 metre press.
			mm	mm	
Volume of gas used (moist)	155·9	17·3° C.	558·7	743·3	24·91
Volume after admission of O (moist)	302·7	17·7	399·0	744·0	93·78
Volume after explosion (moist)	270·2	17·6	433·2	744·2	75·13
Volume after absorption of CO_2 (dry) . . .	246·3	17·8	458·7	744·7	66·13
Volume after admission of H (dry)	522·3	17·9	182·4	745·1	275·80
Volume after explosion (moist)	349·5	18·0	350·5	745·0	124·30

The gas, remaining after diffusion and subsequent absorption of oxygen, therefore contained in 24·91 vols. 15·63 vols. nitrogen and 9·28 vols. combustible gas, which last was a single gas and not a mixture, since it consumed the same amount of oxygen and generated the same amount of carbonic acid after as before diffusion:—

Volume of combustible gas.		Oxygen consumed.		CO_2 generated.
9·28		18·37		9·00
1	:	1·98	:	·97

Experiments Nos. I., II. and III., taken together, enable us to ascertain the volume of the gas which escaped and that of the air which entered during the diffusion experiment; these volumes are as follow:—

Volume of gas escaped . . . . . 86·95
Volume of air entered . . . . . 63·97

Hence, according to the well-known law of diffusion, the specific gravity of the gas must be ·5413.

The gas is therefore hydride of methyl (light carburetted hydrogen), 1 vol. of which consumes 2 vols. oxygen and generates 1 vol. carbonic acid, and the specific gravity of which is ·5528, numbers which correspond almost exactly with those obtained by experiment.

II. A glass jar, graduated in cubic centimetres, was filled with recently boiled distilled water, to which about twenty drops of sulphuric acid had been added, and inverted in a shallow glass dish containing the same liquid; the other bulb was then introduced into the inverted jar, and its capillary extremity broken off against the side of the vessel; the water now slowly gained access to the liquid in the bulb and steady decomposition ensued, the oxide of zinc dissolving as fast as formed, in the dilute sulphuric acid, and the hydride of methyl collecting in the inverted jar. When the decomposition was quite complete, the volume of gas was read off with the usual corrections for temperature and pressure, the graduated jar rinsed out and removed, and the solution of sulphate of zinc in the glass dish, after being evaporated to a smaller bulk, was treated with carbonate of potash and the zinc precipitated as basic carbonate, and weighed as oxide with usual precautions: the following results were obtained:—

·3109 grm. gave ·2660 grm. oxide of zinc, and 138·15 cubic centimetres dry hydride of methyl, at 0° C. and 760 mm. pressure, equivalent to ·0930 grm.

These numbers agree sufficiently with those calculated from the formula

$$C_2H_3Zn,$$

when we consider that every trace of oxygen, which gained admission to the ethereal fluid before its decomposition, would diminish the volume of hydride of methyl, which would also be liable to further diminution, from the solvent action of the fluid over which it was determined:—

	Calculated.		Found.
1 equiv. of Methyl . . .	15	31·56	29·91
1 equiv. of Zinc . . .	32·52	68·44	68·67
	47·52	100·00	98·58

This compound, for which I propose the name Zincmethylium, possesses the following properties:—It is a colourless, transparent and very mobile liquid, refracting light strongly, and possessing a peculiar penetrating and insupportable odour; it is very volatile, but I have not yet been able to determine its boiling-point with accuracy.

Zincmethylium combines directly with oxygen, chlorine, iodine, &c., forming somewhat unstable compounds, a description of which I reserve for a future communication. Its affinity for oxygen is even more intense than that of potassium; in contact with atmospheric air it instantaneously ignites, burning with a beautiful greenish-blue flame, and forming white clouds of oxide of zinc; in contact with pure oxygen it burns with explosion, and the presence of a small quantity of its vapour in combustible gases gives them the property of spontaneous inflammability in oxygen. Thrown into water, zincmethylium decomposes that liquid with explosive violence and with the evolution of heat and light; when this action is moderated, so as to prevent any great rise of temperature, the sole products of the decomposition are oxide of zinc and hydride of methyl,

$$\left.\begin{array}{c} C_2H_3Zn \\ HO \end{array}\right\} = \left\{\begin{array}{c} C_2H_3H \\ ZnO. \end{array}\right.$$

The extraordinary affinity of zincmethylium for oxygen, its peculiar composition, and the facility with which it can be procured cannot fail to cause its employment for a great variety of transformations in organic compounds;[12] by its agency there is every probability that we shall be able to replace oxygen, chlorine, &c., atom for atom, by methyl, and thus produce entirely new series of organic compounds, and obtain clearer views of the rational constitution of others.   I intend to pursue this branch of the subject whilst studying the compounds of zincmethylium and the corresponding bodies containing ethyl and amyl.

Examination of the Gas α.   A quantity of this gas, after standing over sulphuretted water until all traces of iodide of methyl vapour had been absorbed, was transferred into a suitable flask for the determination of its specific gravity; the following numbers were obtained:—

Temperature of room	18·6° C.
Height of barometer	754·2 mm.
Height of inner column of mercury	15·2 mm.
Weight of flask and gas . . .	35·4161 grms.
Temperature in balance case . .	19·6° C.
Weight of flask and dry air . .	35·4500 grms.
Temperature in balance case . .	20·2° C.
Capacity of flask	140·51 cubic centimetres.

From these data the specific gravity was calculated to be ·79598.

---

[12] [Frankland's prediction of the great usefulness of organometallic compounds as alkylating agents proved entirely correct.   Subsequent research indicated the greater convenience of magnesium (Grignard) and lithium reagents.—O.T.B.]

The eudiometrical analysis of the gas gave the following results:—

I. In Short Eudiometer.

	Observed volume.	Temp.	Difference of mercury level mm	Barom. mm	Corrected vol. at 0° C. and 1 metre press.
Volume of gas used (dry)	194·7	18·6° C.	2·1	754·2	137·06
Volume after action of fuming SO_3 (dry)	194·8	18·7	2·2	753·5	137·03
Volume after removal of specimen for combustion (dry)	153·8	19·0	22·0	741·0	103·38
Volume after action of alcohol	82·0	18·7	7·0	741·4	53·72

II. In Combustion Eudiometer.

	Observed volume.	Temp.	Difference of mercury level. mm	Barom. mm	Corrected vol. at 0° C. and 1 metre press.
Volume of gas used (moist)	101·5	18·9° C.	621·7	752·4	10·86
Volume after admission of O (moist)	388·1	18·6	311·7	752·0	154·20
Volume after explosion (moist)	354·6	18·5	345·8	752·2	129·71
Volume after absorption of CO_2 (dry)	321·1	18·3	376·9	752·0	112·88
Volume after admission of H (dry)	745·1	18·7	·8	751·1	523·19
Volume after explosion (moist)	428·3	18·7	274·1	750·5	184·54

III.

	Observed volume.	Temp.	Difference of mercury level. mm	Barom. mm	Corrected vol. at 0° C. and 1 metre press.
Volume of gas used (moist)	104·2	18·8° C.	619·2	750·5	11·23
Volume after admission of O (moist)	371·2	18·9	330·6	750·2	140·04
Volume after explosion (moist)	335·0	18·9	367·7	750·2	114·76
Volume after absorption CO_2 (dry)	299·0	18·2	401·3	750·3	97·83
Volume after admission of H (dry)	707·0	18·4	26·9	750·6	479·33
Volume after explosion (moist)	431·6	18·7	273·4	749·8	185·96

Analysis No. I. proves the absence of all the members of the olefiant gas family, and also that the mixture consists of—

Gas absorbable by alcohol . . . . . . 48·04
Gas unabsorbable by alcohol . . . . . 51·96
_____
100·00

The behaviour of the iodides of ethyl and amyl in contact with zinc,[13] led me to expect that the gaseous products of the decomposition of iodide of methyl by the same metal would consist of methyl, hydride of methyl, and the first member of the olefiant gas series, methylene;[14] but in addition to the proof of the absence of this latter body afforded by the absence of all absorption by fuming sulphuric acid, analyses Nos. II. and III. demonstrate the impossibility of methylene being a constituent of the gaseous mixture; for on constructing three equations in which the volumes of methyl, hydride of methyl, and methylene are expressed, the value obtained for the last gas is invariably a small negative quantity. The volumes of methyl and hydride of methyl are readily found by the two following equations, in which the volume of combustible gas is represented by A, the contraction produced by explosion with excess of oxygen by B, and the volumes of methyl and hydride of methyl respectively, by x and y, the contraction produced by the explosion of methyl and excess of oxygen being 2·5 times its own volume, and that produced by the explosion of hydride of methyl twice its own volume:—

$$x + y = A,$$
$$\frac{5}{2}x + 2y = B.$$

The values of x and y may therefore be thus expressed:—

$$x = 2B - 4A,$$
$$y = 5A - 2B.$$

According to analysis No. II., 10·88 vols. of combustible gas produced a contraction, on explosion with oxygen, equal to 24·49 vols.; and in analysis No. III., 11·23 vols. of combustible gas produced a contraction, on explosion, equal to 25·28 vols. Hence, by

---

[13] Journal of the Chemical Society, vol. ii. p. 265, and vol. iii. p. 30.
[14] [Methylene would be CH_2. In the absence of a valence theory applicable to carbon, and in view of the knowledge of carbon monoxide, CO, such a compound could not be excluded as a possible product.—O.T.B.]

the application of the foregoing equations, the per-centage composition of the gaseous mixture may be expressed as follows:—

	II.	III.	Mean.
Methyl	50·18	50·22	50·20
Hydride of Methyl .	49·82	49·78	49·80
	100·00	100·00	100·00

This result is confirmed by the action of alcohol in analysis No. I., and also by the determination of the specific gravity of the mixed gases, which agrees very closely with that deduced from the above numbers, as is seen from the following comparison:—

Methyl . . . . . $50·20 \times 1·0365 = 52·0323$
Hydride of Methyl[15] . $49·80 \times ·5528 = 27·5294$

$$100·00 \qquad 79·5617$$

$$\frac{79·5617}{100} = ·795617$$

Specific gravity found by experiment . . . . $= ·79598$

The origin of the hydride of methyl in the above gaseous mixture is readily perceived, when the volatility of zincmethylium and the method of collecting the gas are taken into consideration; on opening the decomposition-tube beneath water, a copious effervescence was observed wherever the evolved gas came in contact with water; and as this effervescence was accompanied by the formation of a flocculent precipitate of oxide of zinc, it could only be caused by the presence of the vapour of zincmethylium, which, on coming in contact with water, would be instantaneously decomposed into oxide of zinc and hydride of methyl.

I have not yet endeavoured to procure the methyl free from admixture with hydride of methyl, but have no doubt that, by collecting the gas as evolved from the decomposition-tube over mercury, and absorbing the zincmethylium vapour by dry iodine, the methyl would be left in a state of purity. It perfectly resembles in its properties, chemical and physical, the methyl procured by KOLBE[16] from the electrolysis of acetic acid.[17]

---

[15] [Frankland was completely uninfluenced by Laurent and Gerhardt's reforms and their use of Avogadro's hypothesis. As seen in Frankland's figures, methyl has a density almost twice that of hydride of methyl. Yet he considered the former a radical from which methane was made by *addition* of hydrogen. His "methyl" was in fact ethane.—O.T.B.]

[16] [Kolbe's electrolysis of acetic acid (actually of its metallic salts) also produces ethane.—O.T.B.]

[17] Journal of the Chemical Society, vol. ii. p. 173.

Examination of the Gas β. This gas, evolved by the action of water upon the solid and liquid products of the decomposition of iodide of methyl by zinc, proved, as might have been anticipated, to be pure hydride of methyl, derived from the decomposition of the zincmethylium with which the crystalline residue of iodide of zinc was saturated. Its eudiometrical analysis yielded the following results:—

I. In Short Eudiometer.

	Observed volume.	Temp.	Difference of mercury level.	Barom.	Corrected vol. at 0° C. and 1 metre press.
			mm	mm	press.
Volume of gas used (dry).	168·9	18·6° C.	3·6	750·2	118·05
Volume after action of fuming SO₃ (dry) . .	169·5	18·7	3·7	749·8	118·35

One volume of absolute alcohol, at 19° C. and 732·6 mm. pressure, absorbed ·175 vol. of this gas.

II. In Combustion Eudiometer.

	Observed volume.	Temp.	Difference of mercury level.	Barom.	Corrected vol. at 0° C. and 1 metre press.
			mm	mm	press.
Volume of gas used (moist)	126·7	18·9° C.	595·1	744·9	15·83
Volume after admission of O (moist)	344·9	18·9	357·7	744·8	119·64
Volume after explosion (moist)	295·9	18·9	408·7	744·5	88·44
Volume after absorption of CO₂ (dry) . . .	260·7	18·6	446·1	744·3	72·78
Volume after admission of H (dry)	705·7	18·5	24·6	741·3	473·66
Volume after explosion (moist)	513·0	18·6	193·6	741·1	255·35

These results correspond almost exactly with those yielded by hydride of methyl, 1 vol. of which requires 2 vols. of oxygen for combustion, and generates 1 vol. of carbonic acid.

Volume of combustible gas.		Oxygen consumed.		CO₂ generated.
15·83		31·04		15·66
1	:	1·96	:	·99

By the action of zinc upon iodide of methyl, therefore, two distinct decompositions take place, viz. 1st, the decomposition of iodide of methyl by zinc with the production of iodide of zinc and methyl,

$$\left.\begin{array}{c} C_2H_3I \\ Zn \end{array}\right\} = \left\{\begin{array}{l} C_2H_3 \\ ZnI, \end{array}\right.$$

and 2nd, the decomposition of iodide of methyl by zinc, with the formation of iodide of zinc and zincmethylium,

$$\left.\begin{array}{c} C_2H_3I \\ 2Zn \end{array}\right\} = \left\{\begin{array}{c} C_2H_3Zn \\ ZnI. \end{array}\right.$$

Zincethylium. This body is formed under precisely the same circumstances as zincmethylium, iodide of ethyl being substituted for iodide of methyl; it is a colourless and transparent liquid, refracting light strongly, and having a peculiar penetrating odour; it is less volatile than zincmethylium, and is not so readily prepared pure, owing to its retention of a small quantity of ethyl gas in solution; its affinities are also somewhat weaker than zincmethylium, and it only takes fire in air spontaneously when exposed in considerable quantity. When allowed to absorb oxygen slowly, it forms a white amorphous oxide; it combines also directly with iodine, chlorine and bromine. In contact with water it is instantaneously decomposed into oxide of zinc and hydride of methyl,

$$\left.\begin{array}{c} C_4H_5Zn \\ HO \end{array}\right\} = \left\{\begin{array}{c} C_4H_5,H \\ ZnO. \end{array}\right.$$

Its formula must therefore be

$$C_4H_5Zn.$$

I reserve for a future communication the complete history of this and the following compound.

Zincamylium. This body is generated when iodide of amyl is decomposed by zinc at the temperature of 180° C. It is a colourless and transparent liquid which emits white fumes in contact with the air, but does not spontaneously inflame; it is decomposed in contact with water into oxide of zinc and hydride of amyl,

$$\left.\begin{array}{c} C_{10}H_{11}Zn \\ HO \end{array}\right\} = \left\{\begin{array}{c} C_{10}H_{11}H \\ ZnO. \end{array}\right.$$

From this circumstance, and its analogy with zincmethylium, there can be no doubt that its formula is

$$C_{10}H_{11}Zn.$$

Action of Mercury upon Iodide of Methyl in presence of Light. When iodide of methyl is exposed to sunlight in contact with metallic mercury, it soon becomes coloured red from the separation of free iodine;

after several hours' exposure this coloration disappears, and a small quantity of the yellow iodide of mercury subsides to the bottom of the liquid: after the action of sunlight for several days, the bulk of the mercury is observed to have considerably diminished, and white crystals begin to be deposited around the sides of the glass vessel: finally, after about a week's exposure, the liquid solidifies to a colourless crystalline mass: when this is digested with ether, the new compound dissolves, and is thus separated from metallic mercury, and from the small portion of iodide of mercury which is collaterally formed. Only a very small quantity of gas is evolved during the formation of the white crystalline compound. By spontaneous evaporation the ethereal solution solidifies to a mass of minute colourless crystalline scales: these, dried *in vacuo* and submitted to analysis, yielded the following numbers:—

I. ·3170 grm. dissolved in alcohol and treated with nitrate of silver, gave ·2142 grm. iodide of silver.

II. ·6205 grm. burnt with oxide of copper, gave ·0813 grm. carbonic acid, ·0505 grm. water, and ·5960 grm. protoiodide of mercury. The iodide of mercury, a small portion of which was decomposed into metallic mercury and periodide, collected as an incrustation at the front end of the combustion-tube, about a couple of inches of which had been left empty for this purpose, and projected from the furnace, the heat being so regulated that none of the iodide passed into the chloride of calcium tube, whilst none of the watery vapour condensed in the combustion-tube. When the analysis was concluded, the weight of the protoiodide of mercury, mixed with traces of periodide and metallic mercury, was determined by cutting off the part of the combustion-tube containing it, and ascertaining its weight before and after the iodide was removed. The numbers obtained agree very closely with the formula

$$C_2H_3HgI,$$

which requires the following values:—

	Calculated.		Found. I.	II.
2 equivs. Carbon .	12	3·51	——	3·57
3 equivs. Hydrogen	3	·88	——	·90
1 equiv. Mercury .	200	58·51	——	
1 equiv. Iodine . .	126·84	37·10	36·56	96·05
	341·84	100·00		100·52

This compound is therefore evidently the iodide of a new organo-
metallic body, consisting of one atom of methyl and one atom of
mercury, and for which I propose the name *hydrargyromethylium*: it
is formed by the direct union of one atom of mercury with one atom
of iodide of methyl, under the influence of light,

$$\left.\begin{array}{c} C_2H_3I \\ Hg \end{array}\right\} = C_2H_3HgI.$$

Iodide of hydrargyromethylium is a white solid, crystallizing in
minute nacreous scales, which are insoluble in water, moderately
soluble in alcohol, and very soluble in ether and iodide of methyl;
by the spontaneous evaporation of these solutions the crystals are
again deposited unchanged.   Iodide of hydrargyromethylium is
slightly volatile at ordinary temperatures, and exhales a weak but
peculiarly unpleasant odour, which leaves a nauseous taste upon
the palate for several days; at 100° C. the volatility is much greater,
and the crystals are rapidly dissipated at this temperature when exposed to a current of air.   At 143° C. it fuses and sublimes without
decomposition, condensing in brilliant and extremely thin crystalline
plates.   In contact with the fixed alkalies and ammonia, it is converted into oxide of hydrargyromethylium, which is dissolved by
excess of all these reagents; from these solutions sulphide of ammonium throws down sulphide of hydrargyromethylium as a slightly
yellow flocculent precipitate of a peculiar and most insupportable
odour.   I have not yet further examined the reactions of this
remarkable body, nor have I attempted the isolation of the
hydrargyromethylium.

A corresponding compound containing amyl is formed, though
with difficulty, under similar circumstances, but I have not yet succeeded in producing one containing ethyl, the iodide of this radical
yielding, as I have shown,[18] when exposed to sunlight in contact
with mercury, iodide of mercury, and a mixture of ethyl, hydride of
ethyl and olefiant gases.

I have also made some preliminary experiments with other
metals, and find that most of them are capable of thus entering into
combination with the organic groups, methyl, ethyl, and amyl;
amongst those which thus combine under the influence of light most
readily, and seem to promise the most interesting results, I may
mention arsenic, antimony, chromium, iron, manganese and cad-
mium.   I hope to have the honour of laying before the Royal

---

[18] Journal of the Chemical Society, vol. iii. p. 331.

Society, at an early period, the results of my experiments upon these compounds.

Imperfect as our knowledge of the organo-metallic bodies may yet appear, I am unwilling to close this memoir without directing attention to some peculiarities in the habits of these compounds, which promise at least to throw some light upon their rational constitution, if they do not lead to extensive modifications of our views respecting chemical compounds in general, and especially that interesting class termed conjugate compounds.

That stanethylium, zincmethylium, hydrargyromethylium, &c. are perfectly analogous to cacodyl there can be no reasonable doubt, inasmuch as, like that body, they combine directly with the electronegative metalloids forming true salts, from which, in most cases, and probably in all, the original group can be again separated unaltered, and therefore any view which may be taken of the new bodies must necessarily be extended to cacodyl. The discovery and isolation of this so-called organic radical by BUNSEN was certainly one of the most important steps in the development of organic chemistry, and one, the influence of which upon our theoretical views of the constitution of certain classes of organic compounds, can scarcely be too highly estimated. It was impossible to consider the striking features in the behaviour of this body, without finding in them a most remarkable confirmation of the thoeory of organic radicals, as propounded by BERZELIUS and LIEBIG.

The formation of cacodyl,[19] its habits, and the products of its decomposition, have for some time left no doubt of the existence of methyl ready formed in this body; and KOLBE,[20] in developing his views on the so-called conjugate compounds, has proposed to regard it as arsenic conjugated with two atoms of methyl ($(C_2H_3)_2As$). So long as cacodyl was an isolated example of an organo-metallic body, this view of its rational composition, harmonizing as it did so well with the facts elicited during the route of cacodyl through its various combinations and decompositions, could scarcely be contested; but now, since we have become acquainted with the properties and reactions of a considerable number of analogous bodies,

----

[19] [Frankland here argues that if cacodyl and zinc alkyls are radicals, they should form the same number of oxides as there are states of oxidation for the free metal. However, the highest oxide predicted by this view can never be prepared. Frankland therefore proposes that these so-called radicals are, in fact, stable compounds, and correspond without further combination to the lowest oxidation state of the metals.—O.T.B.]

[20] Journal of the Chemical Society, vol. iii. p. 372.

circumstances arise, which I consider militate greatly against this view, if they do not render it absolutely untenable. According to the theory of conjugate radicals just alluded to, cacodyl and its congeners, so far as they are at present known, would be thus represented:—

Cacodyl	$(C_2H_3)_2As.$
Oxide of cacodyl	$(C_2H_3)_2AsO.$
Cacodylic acid	$(C_2H_3)_2AsO_3.$
Stanmethylium	$(C_2H_3)Sn.$
Stanethylium	$(C_4H_5)Sn.$
Oxide of stanethylium	$(C_4H_5)SnO.$
Stanamylium	$(C_{10}H_{11})Sn.$
Zincmethylium	$(C_2H_3)Zn.$
Zincethylium	$(C_4H_5)Zn.$
Zincamylium	$(C_{10}H_{11})Zn.$
Stibethine (Stibethyl)	$(C_4H_5)_3Sb.$
Binoxide of stibethine	$(C_4H_5)_3SbO_2.$
Oxide of stibmethylium	$(C_2H_3)_4SbO.$
Hydrargyromethylium	$(C_2H_3)Hg.$
Iodide of hydrargyromethylium . .	$(C_2H_3)HgI.$

It is generally admitted, that when a body becomes conjugated, its essential chemical character is not altered by the presence of the conjunct: thus for instance, the series of acids $C_nH_nO_4$, formed by the conjunction of the radicals $C_nH_{(n+1)}$ with oxalic acid, have the same neutralizing power as the original oxalic acid; and, therefore, if we assume the organo-metallic bodies above mentioned to be metals conjugated with various hydrocarbons, we might reasonably expect, that the chemical relations of the metal to oxygen, chlorine, sulphur, &c. would remain unchanged; a glance at the formulæ of these compounds will however suffice to show us that this is far from being the case: it is true that cacodyl forms protoxide of cacodyl and cacodylic acid, corresponding the one to a somewhat hypothetical protoxide of arsenic, which, if it exist, does not seem to possess any well-defined basic character, and the other to arsenious acid; but no compound corresponding to arsenic acid can be formed, and yet it cannot be urged that cacodylic acid is decomposed by the powerful reagents requisite to procure further oxidation, for concentrated nitric acid may be distilled from cacodylic acid without decomposition or oxidation in the slightest degree; the same anomaly presents itself ever more strikingly in the case of stanethylium, which, if we are to regard it as a conjugate radical, ought to combine with oxygen in two proportions at least, to form compounds corresponding to protoxide and peroxide of tin; now stanethylium rapidly oxidizes when exposed to the air and is converted into pure protoxide, but this compound exhibits none of that powerful tendency to combine with an additional equivalent of oxygen, which is so characteristic of protoxide of tin; nay, it may even be boiled with dilute nitric acid without evincing any signs of oxidation: I have been quite unable to form any higher oxide than that described; it is only when the group is entirely broken up and the ethyl separated, that the tin can be induced to unite with another equivalent of oxygen. Stibethyl also refuses to unite with more or less than two equivalents of oxygen, sulphur, iodine, &c., and thus forms compounds, which are not at all represented amongst the combinations of the simple metal antimony.

When the formulæ of inorganic chemical compounds are considered,[21] even a superficial observer is struck with the general symmetry of their construction; the compounds of nitrogen, phosphorus, antimony and arsenic especially exhibit the tendency of these elements to form compounds containing 3 or 5 equivs. of other elements and it is in these proportions that their affinities are best satisfied; thus in the ternal group we have NO_3, NH_3, NI_3, NS_3, PO_3, PH_3, PCl_3, SbO_3, SbH_3, $SbCl_3$, AsO_3, AsH_3, $AsCl_3$, &c.; and in the five-atom group NO_5, NH_4O, NH_4I, PO_5, PH_4I, &c. Without offering any hypothesis regarding the cause of this symmetrical grouping of atoms, it is sufficiently evident, from the examples just given, that such a tendency or law prevails, and that, no matter what the character of the uniting atoms may be, the combining power of the attracting element, if I may be allowed the term, is always satisfied by the same number of these atoms. It was probably a glimpse of the operation of this law amongst the more complex organic groups, which led LAURENT and DUMAS to the enunciation of the theory of types; and had not those distinguished chemists extended their views beyond the point to which they were well supported by then existing facts,—had they not assumed, that the properties of an organic compound are dependent upon the position and not upon the nature of its single atoms, that theory would undoubtedly have contributed to the development of the science to a still greater extent than it has already done; such an assumption could only have been made at a time when the data upon which it was founded were few and imperfect, and, as the study of the phenomena

---

[21] [The author here points out the fallacy that led to the errors of Dumas' substitution law: only atoms of similar combining capacity can take each other's place without disrupting the molecule or greatly altering its properties.—O.T.B.]

of substitution progressed, it gradually became untenable, and the fundamental principles of the electro-chemical theory again assumed their sway. The formation and examination of the organo-metallic bodies promise to assist in effecting a fusion of the two theories which have so long divided the opinions of chemists, and which have too hastily been considered irreconcileable; for, whilst it is evident that certain types of series of compounds exist, it is equally clear that the nature of the body derived from the original type is essentially dependent upon the electro-chemical character of its single atoms, and not merely upon the relative position of those atoms. Let us take, for instance, the compounds formed by zinc and antimony; by combination with 1 equiv. of oxygen the electro-positive quality of the zinc is nearly annihilated; it is only by the action of the highly oxidizing peroxide of hydrogen that the metal can be made to form a very unstable peroxide; but when zinc combines with 1 equiv. of methyl or ethyl, its positive quality, so far from being neutralized, is exalted by the addition of the positive group, and the compound now exhibits such intense affinity for the electro-negative elements as to give it the property of spontaneous inflammability. Teroxide of antimony has also little tendency to pass into a higher state of oxidation; but when its three atoms of oxygen are replaced by the electro-positive ethyl, as in stibethine, that affinity is elevated to the intense degree which is so remarkable in this body.

Taking this view of the so-called conjugate organic radicals, and regarding the oxygen, sulphur or chlorine compounds of each metal as the true molecular type of the organo-metallic bodies derived from it by the substitution of an organic group for oxygen, sulphur, &c., the anomalies above mentioned entirely disappear, and we have the following inorganic types and organo-metallic derivatives:—

Inorganic Types.   Organo-metallic Derivatives.

$$As\begin{Bmatrix} S \\ S \end{Bmatrix} \quad . \quad . \quad As\begin{Bmatrix} C_2H_3 \\ C_2H_3 \end{Bmatrix} \text{Cacodyl.}$$

$$As\begin{Bmatrix} O \\ O \\ O \end{Bmatrix} \quad . \quad . \quad As\begin{Bmatrix} C_2H_3 \\ C_2H_3 \\ O \end{Bmatrix} \text{Oxide of Cacodyl.}$$

$$As\begin{Bmatrix} O \\ O \\ O \\ O \\ O \end{Bmatrix} \quad . \quad . \quad As\begin{Bmatrix} C_2H_3 \\ C_2H_3 \\ O \\ O \\ O \end{Bmatrix} \text{Cacodylic acid.}$$

$$Zn \quad O \quad . \quad . \quad Zn (C_2H_3) \quad \text{Zincmethylium.}$$

Inorganic Types.   Organo-metallic Derivatives.

$\mathrm{Zn}\left\{\begin{matrix} \mathrm{O} \\ \mathrm{O} \end{matrix}\right\}$ . . $\mathrm{Zn}\left\{\begin{matrix} \mathrm{C_2H_3} \\ \mathrm{O} \end{matrix}\right\}$ Oxide of Zincmethylium.

$\mathrm{Sb}\left\{\begin{matrix} \mathrm{O} \\ \mathrm{O} \\ \mathrm{O} \end{matrix}\right\}$ . . $\mathrm{Sb}\left\{\begin{matrix} \mathrm{C_4H_5} \\ \mathrm{C_4H_5} \\ \mathrm{C_4H_5} \end{matrix}\right\}$ Stibethine.

$\mathrm{Sb}\left\{\begin{matrix} \mathrm{O} \\ \mathrm{O} \\ \mathrm{O} \\ \mathrm{O} \\ \mathrm{O} \end{matrix}\right\}$ . . $\mathrm{Sb}\left\{\begin{matrix} \mathrm{C_4H_5} \\ \mathrm{C_4H_5} \\ \mathrm{C_4H_5} \\ \mathrm{O} \\ \mathrm{O} \end{matrix}\right\}$ Binoxide of Stibethine.

$\mathrm{Sb}\left\{\begin{matrix} \mathrm{O} \\ \mathrm{O} \\ \mathrm{O} \\ \mathrm{O} \\ \mathrm{O} \end{matrix}\right\}$ . . $\mathrm{Sb}\left\{\begin{matrix} \mathrm{C_4H_5} \\ \mathrm{C_4H_5} \\ \mathrm{C_4H_5} \\ \mathrm{C_4H_5} \\ \mathrm{O} \end{matrix}\right\}$ Oxide of Stibethylium.

$\mathrm{Sn}\;\;\mathrm{O}$ . . $\mathrm{Sn}\;\;(\mathrm{C_4H_5})$ Stanethylium.

$\mathrm{Sn}\left\{\begin{matrix} \mathrm{O} \\ \mathrm{O} \end{matrix}\right\}$ . . $\mathrm{Sn}\left\{\begin{matrix} \mathrm{C_4H_5} \\ \mathrm{O} \end{matrix}\right\}$ Oxide of Stanethylium.

$\mathrm{Hg}\left\{\begin{matrix} \mathrm{I} \\ \mathrm{I} \end{matrix}\right\}$ . . $\mathrm{Hg}\left\{\begin{matrix} \mathrm{C_2H_3} \\ \mathrm{I} \end{matrix}\right\}$ Iodide of Hydrargyromethylium.

The only compound which does not harmonize with this view is ethostibylic acid, to which LÖWIG assigns the formula $\mathrm{C_4H_5SbO_5}$; but as that chemist has not yet fully investigated this compound, it is possible that further research may satisfactorily elucidate its apparently anomalous composition.

It is obvious that the establishment of this view of the constitution of the organo-metallic bodies will remove them from the class of organic radicals, and place them in the most intimate relation with ammonia and the bases of WURTZ, HOFMANN and PAUL THENARD; indeed, the close analogy existing between stibethine and ammonia first suggested by GERHARDT, has been most satisfactorily demonstrated by the behaviour of stibethine with the haloid compounds of methyl and ethyl. Stibethine furnishes us, therefore, with a remarkable example of the operation of the law of symmetrical combination above alluded to, and shows, that the formation of a five-atom group from one containing three atoms, can be effected by the assimilation of two atoms, either of the same, or of opposite electro-chemical character: this remarkable circumstance suggests the following question:—Is this behaviour common also to the corresponding compounds of arsenic, phosphorus and nitrogen; and can the position of each of the five atoms, with which these elements respectively combine, be occupied indifferently by an electro-negative or an electro-positive element? This question, so important for the advance of our knowledge of the organic bases and their congeners, cannot now long remain unanswered.

If the views which I have just ventured to suggest should be as well borne out by future researches as they are by the facts already known, they must occasion a profound change in the nomenclature of the extensive series of compounds affected by them: I have not, however, ventured to introduce this new system of nomenclature, even in the case of the new bodies described in this memoir, since hasty changes of this kind, unless absolutely necessary, are always to be deplored. In accordance with the suggested view of the constitution of the organo-metallic compounds, the following plan of nomenclature would probably be found most convenient.

Arsenic Compounds.

$(C_2H_3)_2As$	Bimethide of arsenic.
$(C_2H_3)_2AsO$	Bimethoxide of arsenic.
$(C_2H_3)_2AsO_3$	Bimetharsenic acid.
$(C_2H_3)_2AsO_3 + KO$ . .	Bimetharseniate of potash.

Zinc Compounds.

$(C_2H_3)Zn$	Methide of zinc.
$(C_4H_5)Zn$	Ethide of zinc.
$(C_{10}H_{11})Zn$	Amylide of zinc.

Tin Compounds.

$(C_2H_3)Sn$	Methide of tin.
$(C_2H_3)SnI$	Methiodide of tin.
$(C_4H_5)Sn$	Ethide of tin.
$(C_4H_5)SnO$	Ethoxide of tin.
$(C_4H_5)SnCl$	Ethochloride of tin.
$(C_4H_5)SnOSO_3$ . . .	Sulphate of ethoxide of tin.
$(C_{10}H_{11})Sn$	Amylide of tin.
$(C_{10}H_{11})SnO$	Amyloxide of tin.

Antimony Compounds.

$(C_2H_3)_3Sb$	Termethide of antimony.
$(C_2H_3)_4SbO$	Quadromethoxide of antimony.
$(C_4H_5)_3Sb$	Terethide of antimony.
$(C_4H_5)_3SbO_2$	Terethobinoxide of antimony.

Mercury Compounds.

$(C_2H_3)Hg$.   .   .   .   .   Methide of mercury.
$(C_2H_3)HgI$.   .   .   .   Methiodide of mercury.

In naming the new bodies described in the present paper, I have, in conformity with the nomenclature of the organic bases, adopted the principle of employing the termination "*ium*" when the body unites with one equivalent of oxygen, chlorine, sulphur, &c., like ammonium, and the terminal "*ine*" when, like ammonia, it combines with two additional atoms.

5

August Kekulé

The Constitution and Metamorphoses of Chemical Compounds and the Chemical Nature of Carbon

[Translation by O. T. Benfey of "Ueber die Constitution und die Metamorphosen der chemischen Verbindungen und über die chemische Natur des Kohlenstoffs," *Annalen der Chemie und Pharmacie*, *106*, 129–159 (1858). The translation of pages 151–157 of the original (pages 126–130 in this volume) is based in part on the translation by H. M. Leicester and H. S. Klickstein in *A Sourcebook in Chemistry*, Cambridge, Harvard University Press, 1952, pp. 418–421.

The original paper is reprinted in Richard Anschütz, *August Kekulé*, Berlin, Verlag Chemie, 1929, Vol. II, pp. 97–119. It was also reprinted, with commentary, by A. Ladenburg in *Ueber die Constitution und die Metamorphosen der chemischen Verbindungen und über die chemische Natur des Kohlenstoffs. Untersuchungen über Aromatische Verbindungen*, *von August Kekulé* (Ostwald's Klassiker der Exakten Wissenschaften, No. 145), Leipzig, Wilhelm Engelmann, 1904.]

Some time ago[1] I communicated some views[2] "on so-called copulated compounds[3] and the theory of polyatomic radicals," whose further development and completion seems appropriate in order to prevent misunderstanding.

---

[1] *Ann. 104*, 129 (1857).

[2] [The first section represents what Kekulé in 1890 called the "polemical" part, which on later reflection he felt would have been better omitted.—O.T.B.]

[3] [The "so-called copulated compounds," according to Kekulé's article by that name, are complex compounds whose formulas did not fit at the time into any of the general schemes for constructing formulas. In his 1857 article he described how these formulas can be made rational by the combination of several type formulas, whether alike or unlike. The linking of unlike types by polyatomic radicals became known as the theory of mixed types. It was originated by Odling.

For instance, while sulfuric acid is $\mathrm{SO_2''}\left\{ \begin{matrix} H \\ H \end{matrix} \right\} \Theta$, belonging to $\left\{ \begin{matrix} H \\ H \\ H \\ H \end{matrix} \right\} \begin{matrix} \Theta \\ \Theta \end{matrix}$, the double

water type, sulfurous acid belongs to the mixed hydrogen-water type

$\left\{ \begin{matrix} H \\ H \\ H \\ H \end{matrix} \right\} \Theta$ thus $\mathrm{SO_2''}\left\{ \begin{matrix} H \\ H \end{matrix} \right\} \Theta$

—O.T.B.]

My earlier communication led to comments by Limpricht,[4] most of which I do not feel the need to go into.[5] One part, however, requires discussion, since it concerns important theoretical questions. Limpricht claims that there is no justification for my earlier remark "that the view supported by him and v. Uslar leaves unexplained, how, by substitution of ~~SO₂~~ in the place of H, the dibasic sulfoacetic acid is formed from monobasic acetic acid."[6] He says (*Ann. 105*, 182): "We cannot quite understand how according to our view the dibasic nature of this sulfoacid remains unexplained; in fact, any other basicity would be in complete disagreement with our view." I remain of the opinion that the so-called "basicity law"[7] does admittedly allow the prediction to a certain

---

[4] *Ann. 105*, 177 (1858).

[5] As justification for my statements at that time compare: *Ann. 102*, 249: "*new* viewpoint," "is the *new* viewpoint" etc., *Ann. 102*, 259: "It would be a direct contradiction of the facts to continue to consider benzenesulfonic acid as a copulated *sulfuric acid*"; *Ann. 103*, 71: "According to this definition there remain as copulated acids 3) those that are formed from an organic and a dibasic inorganic acid, of which *only* those *copulated with sulfuric acid are known*."

[6] [Using modern formulas, the conversion is that of CH_3CO_2H into $HOSO_2CH_2CO_2H$.—O.T.B.]

[7] This rule, as Strecker (*Ann. 103*, 334) has rightly emphasized in the face of repeated vague citations, stems from him and was only modified by Gerhardt; it is a rule which without doubt holds in many cases and is, therefore, useful; but since the rule has recently been considered as "a generally valid law" it is necessary to draw attention to the fact that this is not so, that the rule only holds when it is not extended too far, namely to those cases to which it does not apply, or if the basicity of the reacting substances or of the product are arbitrarily chosen. A few examples will show this:

Ethylsulfuric acid is monobasic; according to Strecker's (or Gerhardt's) rule it must be monobasic if alcohol is taken as neutral.

Phenylsulfuric acid is monobasic like ethylsulfuric acid; the rule leads to this conclusion if one considers carbolic acid [phenol] as neutral, as phenyl alcohol, if one assumes its basicity to be zero, as in alcohol.

$$B = 2 + 0 - (2 - 1) = 1.$$

The nitroderivatives of carbolic acid are monobasic acids; Limpricht and v. Uslar show (*Ann. 102*, 246f.) with Gerhardt (*Traité* IV, 834) that this must be so because for picric acid, for instance:

$$B = 3 + 1 - (4 - 1) = 1.$$

Now, to obtain these results, the basicity of carbolic acid is taken in one case as equal to unity, in the other as zero. In this way, it becomes possible to fit the rule to both cases and to make it into a "generally valid law" to which at last "the only exception has been discovered" (*Ann. 105*, 185).

Who is to decide whether carbolic acid is an indifferent alcohol or a monobasic acid? If the formation of monobasic phenylsulfuric acid is taken as decisive, so that the basicity of carbolic acid is zero, then picric acid is an exception to the "law." If we proceed the other way, deriving from the formation of picric acid, etc., the view that carbolic acid is a monobasic acid, then phenylsulfuric acid

AUGUST KEKULÉ (1829–1896). From *August Kekulé* by R. Anschütz, Vol. I. Berlin, 1929. Courtesy of the publisher, Verlag Chemie, Weinheim/Bergstr.

becomes an exception; it ought to be dibasic as sulfoacetic acid, for

$$B = 2 + 1 - (2 - 1) = 2.$$

Since, however, it is monobasic, we should probably (cf. *Ann. 105*, 185) seek the reason in yet unexplored properties of carbolic acid. We could, for instance, assume (cf. *Ann. 103*, 80) that there are two carbolic acids, one of which is a monobasic acid while the other is an indifferent body like alcohol.

We find a similar situation in the case of many amide-like compounds. For the amides of monobasic acids, the rule of Strecker as well as that of Gerhardt leads to a basicity of zero. On the other hand, it has been known for some time, that many amides combine directly with a number of metallic oxides, thus behaving as monobasic acids. In the case of acetamide, Strecker himself recently demonstrated this behavior.

For the imides Strecker's rule gives a basicity of zero while Gerhardt's leads to a basicity of one; Strecker cites this (*Ann. 103*, 335) in favor of his rule, and yet we know that succinimide, for instance, forms salt-like compounds with silver oxide and mercuric oxide, while cyanic acid is almost universally considered the imide of carbonic acid, and at the same time as a monobasic acid.

It is evident that the whole question comes to this: What is an acid? Is it a body in which hydrogen can be replaced by a metal, or a body in which such replacement can occur with particular ease? And in the latter case, where is the dividing line? [8]

---

[8] [In Laurent's *Chemical Method*, 1855, p. 212, the following appears: "We perceive that the formation of copulated bodies may be represented by the following formula:

$$xA + yB = C + zAq,$$

in which A represents the acid, B the organic substance acted upon, whether neutral, acid or alkaline, and C the new product. [Here x, y, and z are small integers and Aq represents a molecule of water.] Let us now proceed to a generality pointed out by Gerhardt, under the title of the *law of the saturating capacity of copulated bodies*, which law may be thus expressed:

The capacity of saturation of a copulated body is equal to the sum of the capacities of saturation of the bodies employed, diminished by a single unit:

$$
\begin{array}{ccccccc}
1 & + & 0 & - & 1 & = & 0 \\
\text{Acid} & & \text{Alcohol} & & & & \text{Acetic ether} \\
& & & & & & \text{(neutral)}
\end{array}
$$

$$
\begin{array}{ccccccc}
1 & + & 1 & - & 1 & = & 1 \\
\text{Acid} & & \text{Benzoic acid} & & & & \text{Nitrobenzoic acid} \\
& & & & & & \text{(monobasic)}
\end{array}
$$

But if several molecules of acid or organic compound are employed we must subtract one unit of saturation capacity for each 'copulation.' Thus, for picric acid we must write

$$
\begin{array}{ccccccc}
3 & + & 1 & - & 3 & = & 1 \\
\end{array}
$$
$$3HNO_3 + C_6H_6O - 3H_2O = C_6H_3O(NO_2)_3."$$

The number of copulations is clearly one less than the number of molecules employed in the equation. Thus Strecker's version of the law, as used by Kekulé, adds the total number of combining capacities and subtracts one less than the total number of molecules. Hence Kekulé writes the picric acid equation

$$B = 3 + 1 - (4 - 1) = 1.$$

Laurent was well aware of the limitations of the basicity law, as was Gerhardt. In fact, the same example, the neutral and acid behavior of phenol, was used by Laurent and Kekulé to point up these limitations.—O.T.B.]

degree of the dibasic nature of these acids, *but not the new view* defended by Limpricht and v. Uslar, that sulfoacids are substitution products.

I am now forced to go into this matter a little more fully, something I had earlier intentionally avoided.

In the first place I do not understand what is intended by the phrase "the sulfoacids are substitution products." Substitution has for years been understood to mean the replacement of a number of atoms by an equivalent quantity of other atoms. I do not know in what sense benzenesulfonic acid is to be considered a substitution product of benzene, and sulfocarbolic acid of carbolic acid [phenol]. The SO_2 group is said to enter the radical in place of hydrogen (*Ann.* *102*, 248 and 249); it substitutes. I ask: what does it substitute?

Benzene C_6H_5, H $\qquad$ Benzenesulfonic acid $C_6H_5(SO_2) \brace H \Big\} O$

Carbolic acid $C_6H_5 \brace H \Big\} O$ $\qquad$ Sulfocarbolic acid $C_6H_5(SO_2)O \brace H \Big\} O$

If the interaction of sulfuric acid in the formation of such sulfoacids is considered as a substitution, then, in the first place, the type should be preserved. At least this has been the dominant view since Laurent set up the substitution theory. In these cases, however, the type is changed, and even if this is ignored and only the radicals are considered, as was done in the cases of sulfobenzoic and sulfosalicylic acids, we may well ask: what is substituted in the phenyl radical when benzenesulfonic acid or sulfocarbolic acid is formed? For sulfoacetic acid, sulfobenzoic acid, etc., the assumption was made (*Ann. 103*, 73; *105*, 183 ff.) that the SO_2 group substitutes one *atom* of H although it is *equivalent* to *two* atoms of H. We may perhaps express our expectation that the majority of chemists are not likely to accept such an extension of the concept of substitution. Even this assumption does not make clear why in such a "substitution" (if one wants to use the term, even though it obviously cannot be used) the radical changes its basicity, why from a substance belonging to the H_2O type, a body is formed that belongs to the $2H_2O$ type. Equally unclear is the transformation of a compound belonging to the H_2 type, benzene, into benzenesulfonic acid of the H_2O type through entry of the SO_2 group in place of zero atoms of hydrogen in the radical.

These are the hesitations, expressed in greater detail than earlier, which I indicated in the sentence quoted above. But if the following sentence (*Ann. 103*, 74) is meant to be an explanation (*Ann. 105*, 184), then I cannot concur: "In the case of the remaining substitutions, of which the sulfoacids can be taken as representatives, when an acid radical equivalent to two atoms of hydrogen takes the place of one atom of hydrogen in the organic radical, then the acid radical's equivalent of acid hydrogens, i.e. its basicity is increased by one; the displaced hydrogen atom can, therefore, not be set free." I must admit that I do not completely understand this sentence unless the following is meant by it: One half of the diatomic radical SO_2 takes the place of an atom of hydrogen; but since the other half is not separable from it, not only this half but also the atoms joined with it are held together with this molecular group; and for this reason a substance is formed belonging to a more complicated type. If this is the meaning of the sentence, it is exactly the view that I developed earlier (*Ann. 104*, 141; cf. also Gerhardt, *Traité* IV, 666).

From the above it will be apparent that the agreement among the views concerning copulated compounds (*Ann. 105*, 180) is not very great, and that the differences do not lie largely in the mode of writing of formulas (*105*, 182). Rather, the views themselves show greater divergences than the formulas by which they are expressed. I have no objection to writing benzenesulfonic acid, for instance, as

$$C_6H_5(SO_2) \atop H \Big\} O \qquad \text{instead of} \qquad {C_6H_5 \atop SO_2} \atop H \Big\} O$$

as long as this formula is not meant to imply that benzenesulfonic acid is a substitution product.

I consider this a suitable opportunity for drawing attention to the fact, that, judging by the formulas, now that the typical mode of writing them has become established, there appears to be a greater agreement among the views than is actually the case; some chemists have adopted the outer form of the new type theory completely while misunderstanding the idea underlying it or else interpreting it differently. A simple example will show this. Limpricht, who was the first in Germany to make use in a textbook of the typical mode of writing and of the system based on it (*Grundriss der organischen Chemie* [9]) assumes, for example, as I do, a water type, which we designate H_2O or H_2O_2. The idea which we express by this formula is clearly different even though the formula is the same. Limpricht writes in this connection (*Grundriss*, p. 3 ff.): In the arrangement of the parts of organic compounds a remarkable similarity with certain inorganic compounds is noticed, so that the

---

[9] [Limpricht's *Grundriss* was published by C. A. Schwetschke, Braunschweig, 1855.—O.T.B.]

latter appear as the type of the former. We set up the following types: Hydrogen $=$ H$\}$; Water $=$ H$\}$O$_2$ etc."

He uses O$_2$ for two atoms of oxygen and considers water itself to be HO.[10]   I, on the other hand, designate by the formula H$_2$O, that the simplest compound of hydrogen and oxygen, contains and must contain *two* atoms of hydrogen to *one* atom of oxygen, and that no smaller quantity of this compound can exist since oxygen is *di-*atomic.   I count all compounds as belonging to the same type, in which, through the same cause, that is through a diatomic element (or radical), two monatomic ones are held together to become an indivisible whole, a molecule.   For me the water type only has meaning if the oxygen atoms of Limpricht are an indivisible whole, and, therefore, an atom.   I do not understand how the similarity of organic compounds with water can lead to the view that they belong to the type H$_2$O$_2$, when water itself is taken as HO.   In short, I do not understand the water type, if water does not belong to its own type.

The difference in viewpoint appearing in this simplest of examples is repeated, of course, with all chemical compounds.   It appears even when the formulas by chance are identical.   The fact that this profound difference in viewpoint is apparently pretty generally overlooked, is my excuse for seeking to emphasize it in the following discussion.   In this connection I must emphasize again that I do not consider a large portion of these views as in any way originating with me.   Rather, I am of the opinion that in addition to the chemists mentioned earlier (Williamson, Odling, Gerhardt), whose detailed discussions on these matters are available, there are others who at least share the fundamental ideas underlying these views.   Above all, Wurtz, who never felt it necessary to develop his conceptions in detail, permitted the rest of us to read them between the lines of each of his classical researches.   Without his researches the development of these views would not have been possible.

---

[10] On page 2 (*Grundriss*), the values O $= 16$ and H$_2$O$_2 = 18$ are considered to be the lowest possible effective values (*Wirkungswert*) for organic compounds. The preface on the other hand states the reasons why O $= 8$ is retained and why in the whole book water is designated as HO.   Thus the quantity of water which according to the spirit of the type theory is the least possible is always written as 2HO.

Since Limpricht has not commented on this matter since then, and has continued to write water as HO, we cannot but assume that this remains his view.

For the sake of brevity it seems advisable to forgo citation and criticism of currently held views, in most instances merely to indicate my views, and to curtail as far as possible the number of examples, which in any case can easily be found in any desired number from all classes of compounds.

I regard it as necessary and, in the present state of chemical knowledge, as in many cases possible, to explain the properties of chemical compounds by going back to the elements themselves which compose these compounds.   I no longer regard it as the chief problem of the time, to prove the presence of atomic groups which, on the strength of certain properties, may be regarded as radicals, and in this way to refer compounds to a few types, which can hardly have any significance beyond that of mere pattern formulas.   On the contrary I hold that we must extend our investigation to the constitution of the radicals themselves; that we must ascertain the relation of the radicals to one another and, from the nature of the elements, deduce both the nature of the radicals and that of their compounds.   As my starting point I take the views I developed earlier concerning the nature of the elements and the basicity of the atoms.   The simplest combinations of the elements, as they are determined by the unequal basicities of the atoms, constitute the simplest types.   Compounds may be counted as belonging to a given type, as soon as, in the reaction under observation, the compound is attacked from that particular side which shows the characteristic reaction of the type.   I consider by the term radical the residue that is not attacked in the particular reaction, whose constitution, therefore, is of no concern for the moment.

In order to be more comprehensible, it seems suitable to report first the conception that I have of the process that occurs during chemical metamorphoses.   It seems to me as if the main cause of the lack of clarity in certain points of view is the one-sided conception held about such chemical changes.[11]

Chemical Metamorphoses; Combination and Decomposition.   In earlier periods it seemed sufficient to express the end result of a chemical

---

[11] Cf. also Laurent's ingenious discussion of this matter in *Méthode de Chimie,* p. 408 et al.[12]

---

[12] [Laurent, too, discussed the *process* of reaction and on the page cited described the reaction of benzoyl chloride with ammonia: "To render the reciprocal replacement of the two residues intelligible, I will suppose that in ammonia and chloride of benzoyl the atoms are arranged so as to form hexagonal figures.   Bz and A, Fig. 1, represent chloride of benzoyl and ammonia at the moment when they react upon one another, the face *c* being opposed to the face *h*, which is to be

reaction by an equation; more recently a conception, utilized for long in certain classes of compounds, has been applied universally to all chemical metamorphoses. An attempt was made to conceive all reactions as double decompositions. Gerhardt's type theory rests, as Gerhardt himself emphasizes (*Traité* IV, 586) on the assumption of this reaction, as the reaction type (IV, 570 ff.). I hope it will become clear in what follows, that this conception is not general enough, since it cannot be applied to all metamorphoses, and because even in the cases where it does apply, it does not go far enough in explaining them.

Chemical metamorphoses may be classified for the moment under the following points of view, according to the processes occurring at the time:

(1) *Direct addition* of two molecules to form one, occurs relatively seldom; however, NH_3 adds directly to HCl; PCl_3 to Cl_2, etc. For bodies belonging to the NH_3 type, it is in fact the most characteristic reaction, as they add directly to a molecule of a substance belonging to the H_2 type. The diatomic radicals that have been isolated also add directly to one molecule of Cl_2, etc., e.g. carbon monoxide, elayl,[13] etc.

(2) *Combination of several molecules accompanied by relocation of a polyatomic radical.* The formation of sulfuric acid hydrate from SO_3 and H_2O, of Nordhäuser's oil of vitriol [$H_2S_2O_7$] from anhydrous sulfuric acid and sulfuric acid hydrate, the production of hydrates of dibasic acids when water reacts with the anhydride, the formation of amino acids from the action of water on imides, and of amides when NH_3 acts on imides, etc., belong here. For instance:

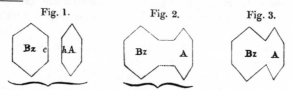

Fig. 1.   Fig. 2.   Fig. 3.

set free. Bz and A, Fig. 2, represent the two residues during the reaction, and Bz, A, Fig. 3, the two residues after the reaction having reciprocally filled up the two voids formed in A and Bz." (A. Laurent, *Chemical Method*, translated by Wm. Odling, London, Cavendish Society, 1855, p. 337.)

Kekulé's debt to Laurent in this discussion is apparent. The passage is probably the first in a chemical journal to contain the hexagon figure—later made popular by Kekulé in his benzene theory.—O.T.B.]

[13] [Elayl is ethylene, C_2H_4.—O.T.B.]

Glycolide	Glycolic Acid	Succinimide	Succinamic Acid	Carbimide (Cyanic Acid)	Carbamide (Urea)

$$
\underset{\text{Glycolide}}{\overset{''}{C_2H_2O}, \ominus}
\left.\begin{matrix} H \\ H \end{matrix}\right\}\ominus
\quad
\left.\begin{matrix} H \\ \overset{''}{C_2H_2O} \end{matrix}\right\{
\begin{matrix} \ominus \\ \ominus \end{matrix}
$$

The reverse occurs in many decompositions, for instance in the formation of the anhydrides of dibasic acids, and in the disintegration of succinamide into ammonia and succinimide. In both cases the number of molecules changes and therefore also the volume in the case of gaseous bodies.[14]

In a far greater number of metamorphoses the number of molecules remains the same (with gases the volume, also). The change can then be considered as if the one molecule has exchanged a portion of its constituent parts for those of another. Among the metamorphoses generally designated:

(3) *Mutual decomposition* or *double exchange*, two essentially different types must be distinguished. First, it is clear, that always equivalent amounts are exchanged, i.e. a *monatomic* against another *monatomic* radical; a diatomic against another diatomic or, alternatively, against two monatomic radicals, etc. If there is exchange of radicals of equal atomicity, the number of molecules remains unchanged; if, however, a diatomic radical is replaced by two monatomic ones, the previously indivisible molecule is split into two smaller molecules because the cause of the connection is lost. Conversely, two previously separate molecules are sometimes united into an indivisible whole (into a molecule) when a diatomic radical takes the place of two that are monatomic.

It is unnecessary to furnish examples for such "double exchange." We may also bypass the further development of views concerning decomposition or combination through the introduction of monatomic in place of polyatomic radicals or vice versa, since these views have been extended by Gerhardt to all classes of compounds in the manner in which I reported them in connection with thioacetic acid.

---

[14] [This sentence makes clear that Kekulé adheres to the "equal volumes, equal molecules" principle of Avogadro and Ampère. The principle was used by Laurent (cf. his *Chemical Method*, pp. 65–68) in his development of consistent formulas. As far as *organic* chemistry was concerned, the reform had been essentially completed *before* the Karlsruhe Congress of 1860.—O.T.B.]

Deserving of emphasis is only that the viewing of such metamorphoses as mutual exchange provides an excellent means for the
recognition of the basicity of radicals (and of the elements).

It cannot be denied that the conception of such metamorphoses
as mutual exchanges at least expresses in the simplest way the relationship of the products to the reactants. However, leaving aside
the above-mentioned additions, this viewpoint is not applicable to a
number of other changes, and in any case does not really give us a
conception of what goes on during the reaction. Rather, it may
(especially in connection with the common expressions: a radical
leaves, is replaced, etc.) lead to the erroneous impression that
during the exchange, while in a sense in transit, the radicals (and
atoms) exist in the free condition.

The simplest conception, and one applicable to all chemical
metamorphoses is the following:

When two molecules react, they first attract each other by virtue
of their chemical affinity, and align themselves next to each other.
The affinities of the individual atoms then cause atoms which previously belonged to different molecules to come into intimate contact. For that reason, the group that was divided in one direction
prior to reaction, now falls apart in another direction, thus:[15]

Before		During		After	
a	b	a	b	a	b
a′	b′	a′	b′	a′	b′

On comparing product and starting material, the decomposition
can be conceived of as a mutual exchange. In the majority of
cases, the force that occasioned the molecules to come together also
causes the resulting decomposition; on the other hand it is conceivable, and cases of this sort exist, that the affinities of the atoms

---

[15] One may consider that during the approach of the molecules to each other,
the connection between the atoms is already loosened, because a part of the force
of affinity becomes bound by the atoms of the other molecule, until at last the
previously united atoms lose their connection altogether, and the newly formed
molecules separate. On this assumption, the conception supplies a certain representation of mass action and catalysis. For in the same manner as a molecule of
one substance acts on a molecule of another substance, so also all other molecules
in the vicinity will act: they loosen the connection among the atoms. The closest
molecule acts most powerfully and suffers double decomposition with the molecule
of the other substance. Those further away aid it; while they loosen the connection of the atoms in the other molecule, they suffer the same change. As soon,
however, as the decomposition has taken place they regain their earlier state.
Mass action and catalysis differ according to this conception only in that in the
case of the former the catalyzing molecule is of the same kind as one of those
decomposing, while in catalysis it is different in substance from both.

belonging to the different molecules will lead to the association of the molecules, but, at least under the same conditions, will not lead to the decomposition of the atomic aggregate so formed into two new molecules.

Of especial interest, therefore, are the cases in which the intermediate state, the molecular aggregate, can be retained, but where by deliberate changes in the conditions the decomposition can be brought to completion. If, for instance, zinc chloride is reacted with alcohol, an addition compound is formed; on heating, decomposition sets in and in most cases follows immediately.

The addition compounds mentioned earlier are such aggregations of two molecules in which, under the particular conditions, the metamorphosis only proceeds to the state preceding the decomposition, that is to the state where the molecules associate. The reaction in a sense remains incomplete. Baeyer's recently discovered behavior of methyl arsenic derivatives toward chlorine shows that this situation holds also for the addition compounds of the NH_3 type. Cacodyl chloride adds directly to chlorine, thus demonstrating the reaction characteristic of the NH_3 type. The product (belonging to the NH_4Cl type) decomposes when mildly heated into methyl chloride and arsenic monomethyl dichloride. Apart from the formation of crystallizable cacodyl trichloride, the reaction appears as a double exchange. But the previously formed addition compound can in this case be obtained with reasonable ease. The arsenic monomethyl dichloride similarly adds chlorine, but the compound thus formed is so easily decomposable, that a freezing mixture must be used to demonstrate that an addition reaction preceded the double exchange.[16]

It is easy to be convinced that this viewpoint is applicable to all metamorphoses that can possibly be thought of as a double exchange. For instance:[17]

---

[16] Such a decomposition probably occurs in the case of all substances belonging to the $NH_3 + HCl$ type; at least the vapor density of ammonium chloride, of phosphorus pentachloride, etc. suggest that these bodies do not vaporize without decomposition, that their vapor in fact is a mixture of two vapors, which recombine when the temperature is lowered, as has been demonstrated with certainty in the case, for instance, of tetraethyl ammonium iodide. [The same view is expressed in the March issue of the *Annalen, 105*, 390 ff.; the present article of Kekulé reached the editors after the closing of that issue but before its publication.—D.R.]

[17] [The reactions represented are the combination of hydrogen and chlorine, the decomposition of mercury cyanide, the hydrolysis of acetyl chloride, and the reaction of ethyl chloride with ammonia to form ethylamine and hydrogen chloride. The reagents are shown left and right; the products are separated by the horizontal line and by a vertical line where necessary.—O.T.B.]

$$\left. \frac{\text{H} \quad \text{Cl}}{\text{H} \quad \text{Cl}} \quad \frac{\text{Hg} \quad \text{Hg}}{\text{CN} \quad \text{CN}} \quad \frac{\text{C}_2\text{H}_3\text{O} \quad \text{H}}{\text{Cl} \quad \text{H}} \right| \text{O} \quad \left. \frac{\text{Cl} \quad \text{H}}{\text{C}_2\text{H}_5 \quad \text{H}} \right\} \text{N.}$$

In addition, a number of reactions seem analogous to all these others, even though they cannot well be considered as double exchanges (unless the hyperoxides are accepted as radicals capable of double exchange, a view to which chemists to date have been unable to agree, even though Laurent has several times demanded it as an obvious conclusion). For instance:

Formation of marsh-gas from potassium acetate and potassium hydroxide

Formation of chloroform from potassium trichloroacetate and potassium hydroxide

$$\left. \frac{\text{CH}_3 \qquad\qquad\qquad \text{H}}{\underset{\text{K}}{\text{C} \text{ OO}} \qquad\qquad \text{K}} \right\} \text{O} \qquad \left. \frac{\text{CCl}_3 \qquad\qquad\qquad \text{H}}{\underset{\text{K}}{\text{C} \text{ OO}} \qquad\qquad \text{K}} \right\} \text{O}$$

Similarly the formation of simple and mixed ketones and of aldehydes:

Acetone

Aldehyde

$$\left. \frac{\text{CH}_3 \qquad\qquad \text{C}_2\text{H}_3\text{O}}{\underset{\text{K}}{\text{C} \text{ OO}} \qquad\quad \text{K}} \right\} \text{O} \qquad \left. \frac{\text{H} \qquad\qquad \text{C}_2\text{H}_3\text{O}}{\underset{\text{K}}{\text{C} \text{ OO}} \qquad\quad \text{K}} \right\} \text{O}$$

The formation also of chloropicrin[18] by reaction of nitric acid with chloral belongs here and appears completely analogous to the formation of chloroform from chloral:

Chloroform

Chloropicrin

$$\left. \frac{\text{CCl}_3 \qquad\qquad\qquad \text{H}}{\underset{\text{H}}{\text{C} \text{ O}} \qquad\qquad \text{K}} \right\} \text{O} \qquad \left. \frac{\text{CCl}_3 \qquad\qquad\qquad \text{NO}_2}{\underset{\text{H}}{\text{C} \text{ O}} \qquad\qquad \text{H}} \right\} \text{O}$$

---

[18] I wish to take this opportunity to report that chloropicrin, whose formation by the distillation of nitric acid, alcohol and salt I reported earlier (*Ann. 101*, 212), can be prepared also: (1) when molten or solid chloral is distilled with concentrated nitric acid or with a mixture of nitric and sulfuric acids, and (2) when a mixture of wood alcohol and sulfuric acid, poured over a mixture of saltpeter and salt, is distilled. Both methods characterize chloropicrin as a methyl derivative; according to the latter, it appears to be methyl chloride whose hydrogen is substituted by chlorine and NO_2; according to the first, as nitrated chloroform or as the nitrite[19] of triply chlorinated methyl.

[19] [The original word here translated as *nitrite* is *Nitrid*. But Kekulé could not possibly have meant nitride as this would not contain oxygen.—O.T.B.]

If the decomposing molecules are more complicated, their cleavage may occur simultaneously in different directions: thus several substances may appear simultaneously as primary products. Thus it becomes unnecessary to assume a series of consecutive reactions.

Effect of Sulfuric Acid on Organic Compounds.   The continuing controversy regarding the constitution and formation of the so-called sulfo acids, etc., makes it appropriate to discuss in somewhat more detail those reactions of sulfuric acid on organic compounds in which so-called copulated compounds are formed.

Three cases may be distinguished:

(1) Several molecules are held together to become an indivisible molecule because the diatomic radical of sulfuric acid rearranges itself in such a way that one half of it takes the place of the *typical* hydrogen.[20] This is by far the most common case; it is exactly the same process which causes the formation of sulfuric acid hydrate from sulfuric acid anhydride and water, and the formation of Nordhäuser's oil of vitriol from sulfuric acid anhydride and hydrate. For instance:

Sulfocarbolic Acid		Benzenesulfonic Acid	
Before	After	Before	After
$\left.\begin{array}{c}\text{C}_6\text{H}_5\\ \text{H}\end{array}\right\}\text{O}$ $\overline{\text{SO}_2,\ \text{O}}$	$\left.\begin{array}{c}\text{C}_6\text{H}_5\\ \text{SO}_2\\ \text{H}\end{array}\right\}\text{O}$	$\left.\begin{array}{c}\text{C}_6\text{H}_5\\ \text{H}\end{array}\right\}$ $\overline{\text{SO}_2,\ \text{O}}$	$\left.\begin{array}{c}\text{C}_6\text{H}_5\\ \text{SO}_2\\ \text{H}\end{array}\right\}\text{O}$

Phenylsulfone

Before	After
$\left.\begin{array}{c}\text{C}_6\text{H}_5\\ \text{H}\end{array}\right\}$ $\overline{\left.\begin{array}{c}\text{H}\\ \text{C}_6\text{H}_5\end{array}\right\}}$ $+ \text{SO}_2,\ \text{O} =$	$\left.\begin{array}{c}\text{C}_6\text{H}_5\\ \text{SO}_2\\ \text{C}_6\text{H}_5\end{array}\right\} + \text{H}_2\text{O}$

Here belongs also the formation of sulfosalicylic acid, a fact to which I drew attention earlier (cf. *Ann. 104*, 149); it should be noted

---

[20] ["Typical" hydrogen is a hydrogen atom belonging to the unsubstituted part of a type formula. Thus benzene $\left.\begin{array}{c}\text{C}_6\text{H}_5\\ \text{H}\end{array}\right\}$ belongs to the type $\left.\begin{array}{c}\text{H}\\ \text{H}\end{array}\right\}$ and phenol $\left.\begin{array}{c}\text{C}_6\text{H}_5\\ \text{H}\end{array}\right\}\text{O}$ to the type $\left.\begin{array}{c}\text{H}\\ \text{H}\end{array}\right\}\text{O}$. One typical hydrogen remains in each formula.

—O.T.B.]

that I demonstrated at that time an analogy between the behavior
of sulfuric acid toward salicylic acid and toward most other organic
compounds (cf. *Ann. 105*, 186).[21]

(2) So far, there have been relatively few cases in which, during
the rearrangement of the atoms, half of the diatomic radical
$-\overset{''}{SO}_2$ takes the place not of the *typical* hydrogen atom, *but of
one atom of hydrogen of the radical*; the attack of the sulfuric
acid on the organic substance occurs, in a sense, from the
other side. Here belong the formation of isethionic
[hydroxyethylsulfonic] acid, of sulfoacetic acid and sulfobenzoic acid, etc.   For instance:

Isethionic Acid		Sulfobenzoic Acid	
Before	After	Before	After

$$
\begin{array}{ll}
\left.\begin{array}{l} \overset{''}{SO}_2, \ominus \\ \hline H \\ \overset{''}{C_2H_4} \\ H \end{array}\right\}\ominus
&
\left.\begin{array}{l} H \\ \overset{''}{SO}_2 \\ \overset{''}{C_2H_4} \\ H \end{array}\right\}\ominus
\end{array}
\qquad
\begin{array}{ll}
\left.\begin{array}{l} \overset{''}{SO}_2, \ \ominus \\ \hline H \\ \overset{''}{C_7H_4}\ominus \\ H \end{array}\right\}\ominus
&
\left.\begin{array}{l} H \\ \overset{''}{SO}_2 \\ \overset{''}{C_7H_4}\ominus \\ H \end{array}\right\}\ominus
\end{array}
$$

(3) Occasionally the action of sulfuric acid on an organic acid
causes the elimination of carbonic acid as in Hofmann and
Buckton's preparation of disulfo acids (or of carbon monoxide
in the formation of Walter's sulfocamphoric acid).

The formation of the disulfo acid of methane can, for
instance, be understood as an exchange of the diatomic $\overset{''}{SO}_2$
for the diatomic $\ominus\ominus$ of the sulfoacetic acid formed earlier.

Sulfoacetic acid $+\overset{''}{SO}_2, \ominus$ yields methanedisulfo acid $+\overset{''}{\ominus\ominus}, \ominus$

$$
\left.\begin{array}{l} CH_2 \\ \overset{''}{CO} \\ \overset{''}{SO}_2 \\ H_2 \end{array}\right\}\begin{array}{l} \\ \ominus + \overset{''}{SO}_2, \ominus \\ \ominus \\ \end{array}
\qquad
\left.\begin{array}{l} CH_2 \\ \overset{''}{SO}_2 \\ \overset{''}{SO}_2 \\ H_2 \end{array}\right\}\begin{array}{l} \\ \ominus + \overset{''}{\ominus\ominus}, \ominus \\ \ominus \\ \end{array}
$$

Radicals, Types, Rational Formulas. From the views expressed
above concerning the process of chemical change my statement
should be clear that "a radical is the unattacked residue in a particular reaction."   It is evident that "depending on whether a decomposition is more or less extensive, radicals of different sizes can

---

[21] It should be noted that the key passage of my earlier article referred, as
can be easily seen from the context, not so much to views concerning sulfo acids,
as to the views often expressed in recent times about amide acids of monobasic
acids and some other amide-like substances.

be assumed." The formation of acetone is of interest in this connection, since two identical molecules supply residues of different
sizes in this reaction. Since the conceptions of radical and of type
complement each other, it becomes plain that the same substance
may also be counted as belonging to different types.[22]

Since, further, the attack on a group of atoms may occur sometimes from the one side and sometimes from the other, a constituent
part will at times have to be taken as belonging to the radical, while
in other reactions it will appear to belong to the type. Even the
very simplest compounds show such varying behavior, and in the
most obvious manner. All cyano compounds, for instance, can in
certain reactions be considered as compounds of the cyano radical
-CN; in other reactions (those in which nitrogen is offered the
opportunity of forming ammonia) they appear as amide-like compounds, i.e. substances belonging to the ammonia type in which H
is replaced by some residue, e.g.:

Prussic Acid	Methyl Cyanide	Cyanic Acid	Urea	Cyanamid	Cyanogen
Nitrile of Formic Acid	Nitrile of Acetic Acid	Imide of Carbonic Acid	Amide of Carbonic Acid	Amide of Imide of Carbonic Acid	Nitrile of Oxalic Acid
$N, \overset{\prime\prime\prime}{C}H$	$N, \overset{\prime\prime\prime}{C_2}H_3$	$N \begin{cases} \overset{\prime\prime}{CO} \\ H \end{cases}$	$N_2 \begin{cases} \overset{\prime\prime}{CO} \\ H_2 \\ H_2 \end{cases}$	$N_2 \begin{cases} \overset{\prime}{C} \\ H_2 \end{cases}$	N_2, C_2*

*-C equivalent to 4H; -C$_2$ equivalent to 6H; see below.

---

[22] Against this view, defended by Gerhardt, repeated opposition has recently
arisen, the remarkable results of Kopp in his researches on specific volumes being
cited against it. A different significance is ascribed to the types than the one they
really carry (according to Gerhardt, etc.); instead of seeing them as expressions of
certain relations during reaction, they are taken as representation of the groupings
of the atoms in the existing compound. Rational formulas are almost ascribed
once more the significance they had earlier, in that they are considered as constitutional formulas rather than reaction formulas. Now it is plain that the
manner in which the atoms emerge from a decomposing and changing substance
cannot possibly prove how they are located in the stable and unchanging substance.
Although it must certainly be considered a task of scientific research to elucidate
the constitution of matter, or, if you will, the location of the atoms, yet we must
admit that it is not the study of chemical reactions but rather a comparative study
of the physical properties of stable substances that can supply means to that end.
Kopp's excellent researches will perhaps yield points of attack for this purpose;
and it may become possible to set up "constitutional formulas" for chemical
compounds, which then of course must be unchangeable. But even when this
is achieved, different rational formulas (reaction formulas) are still permissible,
because a molecule with atoms in given locations can still under different conditions be split in different ways and at different places.

If we consider the decomposition reactions of these substances as "double exchanges" it becomes clear that the so-called radicals are exchanged for an equivalent amount of, for instance, hydrogen. In the action of methyl cyanide on potassium hydroxide solution, for example, the triatomic radical C_2H_3 takes the place of three atoms of hydrogen of which one belonged to the potassium hydroxide, and two to water. In the decomposition of urea, the diatomic radical CO takes the place of two atoms of hydrogen that belonged to two molecules of potassium hydroxide:

Methyl Cyanide   Urea

Before: N, C_2H_3 + H $\Big\}$ $\ominus$ Before N $\Big\{$ $\begin{matrix} H \\ H \end{matrix}$
$\qquad\qquad$ H $\Big\}$ $\qquad\qquad\qquad$ $\overset{''}{CO}$ $\begin{matrix} K \\ H \end{matrix}\Big\}\ominus$
$\qquad\qquad$ H $\Big\}\ominus$ $\qquad\qquad$ N $\Big\{$ $\begin{matrix} H \\ H \end{matrix}$ $\begin{matrix} H \\ K \end{matrix}\Big\}\ominus$
$\qquad\qquad$ K $\Big\}$

After: N, H_3 $C_2H_3 \Big\}\ominus_2$ After: $\begin{matrix} NH_3 \\ \overline{NH_3} \end{matrix}$ $\begin{matrix} K \end{matrix}\Big\}\ominus$
$\qquad\qquad\qquad$ K $\qquad\qquad\qquad\qquad$ $\overset{''}{CO}\Big\{$
$\qquad\qquad\qquad\qquad\qquad\qquad\qquad\qquad$ K $\Big\}\ominus$

Rational formulas are reaction formulas and can be nothing else, in the present state of the science. In that their symbolism indicates the atomic groups that remain unattacked in certain reactions (radicals), or emphasize the constituent parts which play a role in certain often recurring metamorphoses (types), they are intended to provide a picture of the chemical nature of a substance. Every formula, therefore, that expresses certain metamorphoses of a compound, is *rational*; among the different rational formulas, however, that one is the *most rational* which expresses simultaneously the largest number of metamorphoses.

Of the three rational formulas of benzenesulfonic acid:

C_6H_5 $C_6H_5SO_2 \Big\}\ominus$ $C_6H_5SO_3$, H
$\overset{''}{SO_2}\Big\}\ominus$ $\qquad$ H $\Big\}$
H $\Big\}$

the first designates (1) that 1 atom H is easily exchanged for metals, (2) that under the action of PCl_5, chlorine takes up the position of the typical $\ominus$ and, in addition to HCl, the chloride $C_6H_5SO_2$, Cl is formed; it designates (3) that benzenesulfonic acid can be formed from a phenyl and a sulfuryl compound; it therefore expresses all known metamorphoses of this acid and brings to recollection its relations to benzene and sulfuric acid. The second formula expresses only metamorphoses (1) and (2), while the third finally (hydrogen acid theory) designates only salt formation and takes no account of any other reactions. The first is, therefore, by far the most comprehensive and therefore the most rational. The advantages from this point of view of writing formulas according to "mixed types" appears most clearly (in addition to the sulfonic acids) in connection with the more complex compounds of nitrogen.

The formula of an amino acid [23]

$$
\left.\begin{array}{c}
H \\
H \\
\overset{\prime\prime}{C}_2H_2O \\
H
\end{array}\right\}N \atop \Big\}O,
$$

in that it belongs both to the water and ammonia type, shows, for instance, that on the one hand it behaves like a hydrate and on the other as a member of the ammonia type, reacting directly with acids, etc.

The formula of ethyl oxamate similarly shows that from one point of view it appears as an amide, from the other as an ether: [24]

$$
\left.\begin{array}{c}
H \\
H \\
\overset{\prime\prime}{C}_2O_2 \\
C_2H_5
\end{array}\right\}N \atop \Big\}O
$$

The formulas generally in use so far:

$$
\left.\begin{array}{c}
NH_2\ (\overset{\prime\prime}{C}_2O_2) \\
C_2H_5
\end{array}\right\}O \quad \text{and} \quad N\left\{\begin{array}{c}
C_2O_2,\ C_2H_5,\ O \\
H \\
H
\end{array}\right.
$$

of which one represents ethyloxamate as an ether of oxamic acid, the other as the amide of ethyloxalic acid, are in fact only condensed expressions of this formula from different points of view. Both are rational formulas correct for a particular class of reactions; the representation according to mixed types is a combination of both and thus gives the most complete picture.

In general the most resolved formula will express the nature of a body most completely. If, therefore, we normally prefer a more

---

[23] [The formula shown is that of glycine, $NH_2CH_2CO_2H$.—O.T.B.]

[24] [By *ether* was meant both alkyl ethers ROR' and acyl alkyl ethers or esters RCO.OR'.—O.T.B.]

empirical formula, expressing the most common reactions, we must still admit that the other is more rational.[25]

The Constitution of Radicals and the Nature of Carbon. It has often been emphasized that radicals are not groups of atoms inherently more closely bound together, but only atoms located near each other, which in certain reactions do not separate, while in others they break apart. It depends on the nature of the atoms which are located together and on the nature of the reacting substance whether or not an atom group plays the part of a so-called "radical," whether it is a more or less stable radical. In general it can be said that the greater the difference in the nature of the individual atoms, the more easily will an atomic group or a radical break apart.

It will not be necessary to extend these considerations further; I will give only one example to show how this association of atoms can occur. The radical of sulfuric acid SO_2 contains three atoms, each of which is diatomic, thus representing two affinity units. On joining together, one affinity unit of one atom combines with one of the other. Of the six affinity units, four are thus used to hold the three atoms themselves together; two remain over, and the group appears as diatomic; it unites, for instance, with two atoms of a monatomic element:

Sulfuryl Radical   Sulfuryl Chloride

---

[25] For acetic acid, for instance, the formula $\left.\begin{array}{c}C_2H_3O \\ H\end{array}\right\}O$ is generally used; according to its formation from acetonitrile (and the formation of formic acid from chloroform $C'''H, Cl_3$) it has the formula $\left.\begin{array}{c}C_2H_3 \\ H\end{array}\right\}O_2$ and then becomes comparable with metaphosphoric acid. Finally, a number of decompositions form carbonic acid or another compound of the CO radical; acetic acid can then be regarded as (cf. Mendius *Ann. 103*, 80):

$$\begin{array}{cc} CH_3 & C_6H_5 \\ \left.\begin{array}{c}CO \\ H\end{array}\right\}O & \left.\begin{array}{c}SO_2 \\ H\end{array}\right\}O \end{array}$$

It then appears analogous to benzenesulfonic acid (as methylcarbonic acid). The remarkable preparation of propionic acid by action of carbon dioxide on ethylsodium, which has very recently been discovered by Wanklyn, can then be understood in the same way as the formation of benzenesulfonic acid from benzene and sulfuric acid anhydride.

If the sulfuryl chloride now acts on water, 2 HCl split off, the residues remain combined, and the resulting product can be considered as two molecules of ~~H_2O~~ in which two atoms of H are replaced by the group ~~SO_2~~.[26]

The manner in which the atoms are associated in all other radicals, including those containing carbon, can be conceived in a similar way. To do the latter, it is only necessary to form a picture of the nature of carbon.

If only the simplest compounds of carbon are considered (marsh gas, methyl chloride, carbon tetrachloride, chloroform, carbonic acid, phosgene gas, carbon disulfide, prussic acid, etc.), it is striking that the amount of carbon which the chemist has known as the smallest possible, as the *atom*, always combines with four atoms of a monatomic, or two atoms of a diatomic element; that in general, the sum of the chemical units [27] of the elements which are bound to one atom of carbon is equal to 4. This leads to the view that carbon is *tetratomic* (or tetrabasic).[28]

Accordingly, carbon takes its place with the three groups of elements mentioned earlier as the only representative yet known of a fourth group (the compounds of boron and silicon being still too little known). Its simplest combinations with elements of the three other groups are: [29]

$$IV + 4I \qquad\qquad IV + 2II$$
$$IV + (II + 2I) \qquad\qquad IV + (III + I)$$

or, in examples,

~~CH_4~~	~~$COCl_2$~~	~~CO_2~~	~~CNH~~
~~CCl_4~~		~~CS_2~~	
~~CH_3Cl~~			
~~$CHCl_3$~~			

---

[26] It can easily be seen that the group ~~SO~~, which under certain conditions plays the part of a radical, must also be diatomic. Sulfurous acid (as the hydrate), which according to one view contains the same radical as sulfuric acid and belongs to the intermediate type $H_2 + H_2O$, is, according to another, one of the compounds of the radical ~~SO~~, belonging to the type ~~$2H_2O$~~. The two expressions are, in a sense, synonymous.

[27] [Chemical units are affinity units based on the affinity unit of H = 1.—O.T.B.]

[28] If carbon is introduced into the types as a *tetratomic radical*, relatively simple formulas are obtained for some well-known compounds. It would, however, lead too far to go further into this.

[29] [The Roman numerals refer to affinity units of atoms or radicals.—O.T.B.]

In the cases of substances containing several atoms of carbon, one must assume that some at least of the atoms are held in the compound in the same way (as in the cases already quoted) by the affinity of the carbon, and that the carbon atoms themselves align themselves next to each other, whereby a portion of the affinity of the one carbon atom is, of course, bound by an equal portion of the affinity of the other.

The simplest and therefore most probable case of this association of two carbon atoms is that in which one unit of affinity of the one carbon atom is combined with one unit of affinity of the other. Of the 2×4 units of affinity of the two carbon atoms, two are used in holding the two atoms together; there remain, therefore, six which may be held in combination by atoms of other elements. In other words the group of two carbon atoms, C_2, is hexatomic; it will form a compound with 6 atoms of a monatomic element, or in general with that number of atoms that will make the sum of their chemical [affinity, *Transl.*] units $=6$ (e.g. ethyl hydride, ethyl chloride, ethylene dichloride, $1\frac{1}{2}$carbon tetrachloride [C_2Cl_6, *Transl.*], acetonitrile, cyanogen, acetaldehyde, acetyl chloride, glycolide, etc.).

If more than two carbon atoms unite in this way, the basicity of the carbon group will be increased by two units for each additional carbon atom. Thus the number of hydrogen atoms (chemical units) which may be combined with n carbon atoms is expressed by

$$n(4-2)+2 = 2n+2.$$

For $n=5$, the basicity is 12 (amyl hydride, amyl chloride, amylene chloride, valeronitrile, valeraldehyde, valeryloxide, angelic acid, pyrotartaric acid anhydride, etc.).

Up to this point we have assumed that all the atoms attaching themselves to carbon are held by the affinity of the carbon. It is equally conceivable, however, that in the case of polyatomic elements (Θ, N, etc.) only a part of the affinity of these—for example, only one of the two units of affinity of the oxygen, or only one of the three units of the nitrogen—is attached to carbon; so that one of the two units of affinity of the oxygen, and two of the three units of affinity of the nitrogen, remain over and may be united with other elements. These other elements are therefore only in indirect union with carbon, a fact which is indicated in the typical mode of writing the formulas:

$$\left.\begin{array}{c} C_2H_5 \\ H \end{array}\right\}\Theta \qquad \left.\begin{array}{c} C_2H_5 \\ H \\ H \end{array}\right\}N \qquad \left.\begin{array}{c} C_2H_3O \\ C_2H_5 \end{array}\right\}\Theta \qquad \left.\begin{array}{c} C_2H_5 \\ C_2H_5 \\ C_2H_5 \end{array}\right\}N$$

In like manner several carbon groups can be held together by oxygen or nitrogen atoms.

When such compounds are considered, particularly with regard to those atoms which are linked in this way to the carbon group, then the carbon group appears to be a radical, and we can say that the radical replaces one atom of H of the type, because instead of its one atom of H the affinity of $\ominus$ or N would be saturated in its place.

When comparisons are made between compounds which have an equal number of carbon atoms in the molecule and which can be converted into each other by simple transformations (e.g. alcohol, ethyl chloride, acetaldehyde, acetic acid, glycolic acid, oxalic acid, etc.) the view is reached that the carbon atoms are arranged in the same way and only the atoms held to the carbon skeleton are changed.

When, on the other hand, homologous bodies are considered, the conclusion is reached that in these the carbon atoms (regardless of how many are held in a molecule) are arranged together in the same manner, according to the same laws of symmetry. In more far-reaching decompositions, in which the carbon skeleton itself is attacked and broken into fragments, each fragment shows the same arrangement of carbon atoms, so that each fragment of the compound is homologous with the starting substance or can be obtained from a body homologous with it by a simple transformation (e.g., replacement of hydrogen by oxygen).

In a great many organic compounds such a "simplest" alignment of carbon atoms can be assumed. Others contain so many carbon atoms in the molecule that for them a denser arrangement of carbons must be assumed.[30]

Benzene, for example, and all its derivatives, as well as the hydrocarbons homologous with it, show such a high carbon content as to differentiate these bodies characteristically from all the substances related to ethyl.

Naphthalene contains still more carbon. The carbon must be assumed to be arranged in a still denser form, that is, the individual atoms are still more closely held together.

When these carbon-rich hydrocarbons, benzene and its homologs and naphthalene, are compared with the hydrocarbons of the alcohol group (elayl and its homologs) with which they show analogies in many respects, we have:

---

[30] It is easy to be convinced that the formulas of these compounds can be constructed through the "next simplest" arrangement of carbon atoms.

Ethylene	Propylene	Butylene	Amylene
C_2H_4	C_3H_6	C_4H_8	C_5H_{10}

	Benzene	Toluene	Xylene
	C_6H_6	C_7H_8	C_8H_{10}

Naphthalene
$C_{10}H_8$

Comparing the hydrocarbons of the second row with those of the first, it is found that with an equal hydrogen content, they contain three more carbons. Between naphthalene and toluene the same relation occurs. It thus seems as if here the same sort of denser arrangement of carbon atoms is repeated and as if there were three classes of carbon-containing compounds differentiated from each other by the type of arrangement of carbon atoms.

Principles of a Classification of Organic Compounds. From the considerations expressed above, a classification of carbon compounds can be deduced which I wish to describe at the end because, having used it for a considerable period of time, it seems to me to provide a reasonably clear organization of the compounds of carbon. I hope this classification will be found not only clear but also in conformity with the time, since it is built on the most important discoveries of the last few years.

I first divide organic compounds into three (already mentioned) classes according to their carbon content, and employ for their grouping within these classes:

(1) The transition of monatomic to polyatomic radicals through the loss of hydrogen;
(2) The replacement of hydrogen in a radical by oxygen;
(3) The homologous series.

The following table, in which for the sake of simplicity I group the radicals, will clarify the system.

Group 1 Covers the alcohols and their derivatives;
      2 The fatty acids, etc.;
      3 The homologs of olefiant gas, glycols, etc.;
      4 Carbonic acid, glycolic acid, lactic acid, etc.;
      5 Oxalic acid, succinic acid and their homologs;
      6 Chloroform, glycerols, etc., as well as allyl alcohol, etc.;
      7 Acrolein, acrylic acid and their homologs, etc.

Monatomic Radicals	Group 1 C_nH_{2n+1}	Group 2 $C_nH_{2n-1}O$	
	$'CH_3$	$'CHO$	
	$'C_2H_5$	$'C_2H_3O$	
	$'C_3H_7$	$'C_3H_5O$	
	$'C_4H_9$	$'C_4H_7O$	
Diatomic Radicals	Group 3 C_nH_{2n}	Group 4 $C_nH_{2n-2}O$	Group 5 $C_nH_{2n-4}O_2$
	$''CH_2$	$''CO$	—
	$''C_2H_4$	$''C_2H_2O$	$''C_2O_2$
	$''C_3H_6$	$''C_3H_4O$	—
	$''C_4H_8$	—	$''C_4H_4O_2$
Triatomic Radicals (also monatomic)	Group 6 C_nH_{2n-1}	Group 7 $C_nH_{2n-3}O$	
	$'''CH$		
	$'''C_2H_3$		
	$'''C_3H_5$	$'C_3H_3O$	

Lastly, I feel bound to emphasize that I myself attach but a subordinate value to considerations of this kind. But since in chemistry, when there is a total lack of exact scientific principles to go on, we have to content ourselves for the time being with conceptions of probability and expediency, it appears appropriate that these views should be published, because they seem to me to furnish a simple and reasonably general expression precisely for the latest discoveries, and because, therefore, their application may perhaps conduce to the discovery of new facts.

Heidelberg, March 16, 1858

6

Archibald Scott Couper

On a New Chemical Theory

[From *On a New Chemical Theory and Researches on Salicylic Acid. Papers by Archibald Scott Couper*, Edinburgh, The Alembic Club, 1953, 9–13; translation by Leonard Dobbin of "Sur une Nouvelle Théorie Chimique," *Comptes rendus de l'Académie des Sciences*, 46, 1157–1160 (1858). The paper was presented to the Academy by Dumas.]

I have the honour to lay before the Academy the principal features of a new chemical theory that I propose for organic combinates.

I go back to the elements themselves, of which I study the mutual affinities. This study is, in my opinion, sufficient for the explanation of all chemical combinates, without it being necessary to revert to unknown principles and to arbitrary generalizations.

I distinguish two species of affinity, namely:

1°. Affinity of degree;   2°. Elective affinity.

By affinity of degree, I mean the affinity that one element exerts upon another with which it combines in several definite proportions. I call elective affinity that which different elements exert with different intensities upon one another. Taking carbon for example, I find that it exerts its combining power in two degrees. These degrees are represented by CO^2 and CO^4, that is to say by oxide of carbon and carbonic acid, adopting for the equivalents of carbon and of oxygen the numbers 12 and 8.

So far as concerns its elective affinities, carbon differs from the other elements and exhibits, so to speak, a special physiognomy. The features that characterise this elective affinity of carbon are the following:

1°. It combines with equal numbers of equivalents of hydrogen, of chlorine, of oxygen, of sulphur, etc., which can mutually replace one another so as to satisfy its combining power.

2°. It enters into combination with itself.

These two properties suffice, in my opinion, to explain all that is presented as characteristic by organic chemistry. I believe that the second is pointed out here for the first time. In my opinion it accounts for the important and still unexplained fact of the accumulation of molecules of carbon in organic combinates. In these com-

ARCHIBALD SCOTT COUPER (1831–1892).
From *Proceedings of the Royal Society of Edinburgh,*
Vol. 29, 1909.   Courtesy of the Royal Society of
Edinburgh.

pounds where 2, 3, 4, 5, 6, etc., molecules[1] of carbon are bound together, it is carbon which serves as link to carbon.

It is not hydrogen that can bind together the elements of organic bodies. If, like carbon, it had the power to combine with itself, it would be possible to form the compounds H^4Cl^4, H^6Cl^6, H^8Cl^8.[2]

So far as oxygen is concerned, I admit that an atom of this body in combination exerts a powerful affinity upon a second atom of oxygen that is itself combined with another element. This affinity is modified by the electrical position of the elements to which the atoms of oxygen are respectively attached. The following explanations will make this conception understood.

The highest combining power known for carbon is that of the second degree, that is to say 4.

The combining power of oxygen is represented by 2.

All the combinates of carbon can be referred to two types. One of these is represented by the symbol[3]

$$nCM^4,$$

the other by the symbol

$$nCM^4 - mM^2$$

where m is $< n$, or else $nCM^4 + mCM^2$, where n can become nil. As examples of the first type, the alcohols, the fatty acids, the glycols, etc., may be cited.

Methylic and ethylic alcohols will be represented by the formulæ[4]

$$C\begin{cases} O...OH \\ H^3, \end{cases} \qquad \begin{matrix} C \begin{cases} O...OH \\ ...H^2 \end{cases} \\ \vdots \\ C...H^3. \end{matrix}$$

It will easily be seen that for methylic alcohol the limit of combination of the carbon is equal to 4, the carbon in it being combined

---

[1] [Couper is using the words atom and molecule interchangeably.—O.T.B.]

[2] [Couper, for complex reasons, retains O=8, but insists that almost invariably two oxygen atoms remain together. If these pairs are written as single oxygen atoms of atomic weight 16, his formulas become very similar to ours.—O.T.B.]

[3] [These formulas were misunderstood both by Kekulé, in his immediate rebuttal of Couper's views (*Compt. rend.*, 47, 378 (1858)), and by Butlerov. M is not an atom, but an affinity unit. Therefore nCM^4 represents any compound in which all carbon atoms are attached to four different atoms or groups. On the other hand, unsaturated compounds are represented by $nCM^4 - mM^2$. In other words, affinity units are lost in pairs. We now say that double and triple bonds or rings are formed.—O.T.B.]

[4] [These formulas represent Couper's first tentative introduction of the valence line uniting atoms. Only William Higgins (cf. E. R. Atkinson, *J. chem. Educ.*, 17, 3 (1940)), before Couper, used lines for such purposes, but Higgins' approach of 1789 never made contact with organic chemistry.—O.T.B.]

with 3 of hydrogen and with 1 of oxygen. This oxygen, of which the combining power is equal to 2, is in turn combined with another atom of oxygen, itself united to 1 of hydrogen.

In the case of ordinary alcohol, each of the two atoms of carbon satisfies its combining power, on the one hand, by uniting with 3 atoms of hydrogen or of hydrogen and oxygen, and, on the other hand, by uniting with the other atom of carbon. The oxygen is combined in the same manner as in the preceding example. In these cases it will be seen that the carbon belongs to the first type, each atom being combined in the second degree.

In propylic alcohol,
$$C \begin{cases} O...OH \\ H^2 \end{cases}$$
$$\vdots$$
$$C...H^2$$
$$\vdots$$
$$C...H^3,$$

the combining power of the atom of carbon that is situated in the middle is reduced to 2 for hydrogen, since it is combined chemically with each of the two other atoms of carbon.

Formulæ analogous to those preceding, express the constitution of the other alcohols.

The constitution of ether is represented by the formula
$$C \left\{ \begin{matrix} O...O \\ H^2 \; H^2 \end{matrix} \right\} C$$
$$\vdots \qquad \vdots$$
$$C...H^3 \; H^3...C.$$

Formic acid is
$$C \begin{cases} O...OH \\ O^2 \\ H, \end{cases}$$

acetic acid
$$C \begin{cases} O...OH \\ O^2 \end{cases}$$
$$\vdots$$
$$C...H^3.$$

The constitution of glycol is represented by the formula
$$C \begin{cases} O...OH \\ H^2 \end{cases}$$
$$\vdots$$
$$C \begin{cases} H^2 \\ O...OH, \end{cases}$$

that of oxalic acid by the formula
$$C \begin{cases} O...OH \\ O^2 \end{cases}$$
$$\vdots$$
$$C \begin{cases} O^2 \\ O...OH, \end{cases}$$

or, if it is desired to join the negative oxygen to one of the poles of the molecule, by the formula

$$C \begin{cases} O^2 \\ O^2 \end{cases}$$
$$\vdots \\ C \begin{cases} O...OH \\ O...OH. \end{cases}$$

Be that as it may, however, it can be seen according to this theory that, in the constitution of organic acids of the first type, the presence of 2 atoms of oxygen combined together in such a manner that both are attached directly to carbon and situated near the negative oxygen—that is to say, near the oxygen which carries along with it the oxygen raised to an electro-positive state by its combination with one atom of a relatively electro-positive element; that the presence, I say, of these atoms of oxygen is necessary in order that the negative oxygen may find itself in that electrical state which gives to the body the properties generally described by the name of *acids*.

This is a particular case of a general law; because it can be seen, according to this theory, how the electro-positive or electro-negative value of the elements mutually modifies and conditions the electro-positive or electro-negative value of the other elements.

This law differs from the electric hypothesis that chemists have hitherto defended, but which has never been able to receive a complete application to their views on organic chemistry; that, on the contrary, which I advance, agrees perfectly with the application of the theory that I propose, to the facts.

There remains nothing for me but to add the manner in which I formulate salicylic acid and the terchlorophosphate of salicyl which I made known in a communication submitted to the Academy at its last sitting.

Salicylic acid

$$C \begin{cases} C...H^2 \\ C...H \end{cases}$$
$$\vdots \\ C \begin{cases} C...H \\ C...O...OH \end{cases}$$
$$\vdots \\ C \begin{cases} O^2 \\ O...OH \end{cases}$$

Terchlorophosphate of salicyl

$$C \begin{cases} C...H^2 \\ C...H \end{cases}$$
$$\vdots \\ C \begin{cases} C...H \\ C...O...O \end{cases}$$
$$\vdots \\ C \begin{cases} O^2 \\ O...O \end{cases} \Bigg\} PhCl^3$$

These formulæ suffice, for the moment, to indicate my ideas on the constitution of the bodies.

7

Archibald Scott Couper

On a New Chemical Theory

[From *Proceedings of the Royal Society of Edinburgh*, *29*, 240–264 (even pages only) (1909).

This paper was originally published in *The Philosophical Magazine and Journal of Science*, [4], *16*, 104–116 (1858), but was little noticed on the Continent. It was discovered by Richard Anschütz (Kekulé's biographer; cf. L. Dobbin, "The Couper Quest," *J. chem. Educ.*, *11*, 331 (1934)), and was reprinted at his suggestion in the *Proceedings of the Royal Society of Edinburgh* in the version reproduced here (some of the original typographical errors were corrected).]

The end of chemistry *is its theory*. The guide in chemical research *is a theory*. It is therefore of the greatest importance to ascertain whether the theories at present adopted by chemists are adequate to the explanation of chemical phenomena, or are, at least, based upon the true principles which ought to regulate scientific research.

Among those which have lately been developed, there is one, on account of its apparently numerous merits, which particularly claims investigation, and respecting which we deem that it would not be unprofitable were either new proofs of its scientific value furnished, or, on the contrary, should considerations be adduced establishing not only its inadequacy to the explanation, but its ultimate detriment to the progress of science. I allude to the system of types as advocated by Gerhardt.

This system, striking alike for the breadth of its conception, and the logical and consequent manner in which it has been developed, has been controverted from the point of view afforded by theories less far-reaching than the one under consideration, and even based upon a one-sided and restricted appreciation of certain chemical reactions. The consequence is that this opposition has not impaired the favour with which the unitary system has been received, but has rather tended to display it in a more advantageous light.

Imposing as this theory is, it is nevertheless all the more necessary to submit it to a strict investigation; for there is nothing so prejudicial in the search for truth as the blind spirit of conservation. A rational belief demands the test of a preliminary doubt.

There are two conditions which every sound theory must fulfil:—

1. It must be proved to be empirically true.
2. It must no less be philosophically true.

I admit that this theory is for the most part empirically true; that is to say, it is not contradicted by many of the facts of the science. Evidence that this condition is only partially fulfilled, is to be found—

1. In the circumstance that the peroxides, for instance, do not fit very satisfactorily into the types.

2. The principle of double decomposition cannot well be applied to the conversion of the anhydrous sulphuric acid into the hydrate of that acid by the action of one equivalent of water, the formulæ of these bodies being, according to Gerhardt, in their free state $O.SO^2$ and H^2O. Combined, they become simple SH^2O^4.

The same remark applies in like manner to carbonic acid. In these instances the wonted consequence of Gerhardt is missed. The fact of the density of the vapour of these bodies being the same in the free as in the combined states, may have prevented him from doubling the formulæ of these anhydrous acids. The types of this theory being *essentially types of* double *decomposition*, this instance of a simple combination diminishes somewhat the value of the otherwise great logical merit of this system.

Having taken notice of such exceptions, the empirical truth of the theory may be otherwise admitted.

The philosophical test[1] demands that a theory be competent to explain the greatest number of facts in the simplest possible manner.

In applying this test, three aspects of it require to be taken into consideration:—

1. As to the extension of the theory.
2. The explanation it affords of the facts.
3. The manner of this explanation.

As to the first: this theory indeed brings every chemical combinate under a certain comparative point of view with every other. Herein apparently is its merit. Nevertheless, should our test be applied to its full extent, it will be found that it is fatal to this system, in other respects so imposing. The comparative point of view which it adopts is fundamentally false.

As to the second: it does not explain the facts at all; consequently the most essential point of the test is unfulfilled.

3. This condition of the test is in like manner unfulfilled from the fact of the second not being complied with.

---

[1] [Couper had studied philosophy in Glasgow and Edinburgh.—O.T.B.]

Why is it that Gerhardt's theory so signally fails in these two essential requisites? Because it is based upon an old but vicious principle, which has already retarded science for centuries. It begins with a generalization, and from this generalization deduces all the particular instances. But it does not come within the limits of a chemical paper to enter upon a discussion which is purely metaphysical. Nevertheless, the theory of Gerhardt can only be combated upon metaphysical grounds, because it is only in overturning a general principle of research that the theory can be proposed. Gerhardt's generalization lacks, moreover, the merit of being represented by a type having a known existence. nO_H^H, from which he derives every chemical combinate, being in itself indefinite, cannot of course be contained or be produced in any definite body. That, however, which may be demanded of the type is, that in itself it should afford at least an instance of that which it is meant to represent. Now the part "n" of the type represents the notion of indefinite multiples of O_H^H. But not a single instance of a multiple of O_H^H has been proved to exist; much less has it been proved that there exists, or can exist, multiples of this body in an indefinite series. The perfection or imperfection of the type meant to represent the generalized notion is, however, a matter of comparatively inferior moment. It is the principle involved in this generalization which is essentially pernicious.

Should the principle which is therein adopted be applied to the common events of life, it will be found that it is simply absurd. Suppose that some one were to systematize the formation of letters into words that formed the contents of a book. Were he to begin by saying that he had discovered a *certain word which would serve as a type, and from which by substitution and double decomposition all the others are to be derived,*—that he by this means not only could form new words, but new books, and books almost *ad infinitum,*—that this word also formed an admirable point of comparison with all the others,— that in all this there were only a few difficulties, but that these might be ingeniously overcome,—he would state certainly an empirical truth. At the same time, however, his method would, judged by the light of common sense, be an absurdity. But a principle which common sense brands with absurdity, is philosophically false and a scientific blunder.

Suppose the book that had formed the basis of this system were a a German one, where all the words were found to be composed at least of two letters, still even in this language the viewing and systematizing of words as a series of double decompositions would be no less ridiculous.

The sure and invincible method of arriving at every truth which the mind is capable of discovering is always one and the same. It is that, namely, of throwing away all generalization, of going back to first principles, and of letting the mind be guided by these alone. It is the same in common matters. It is the same in science. To reach the structure of words [2] we must go back, seek out the undecomposable elements, viz., the letters, and study carefully their powers and bearing. Having ascertained these, the composition and structure of every possible word is revealed. It would be well to call to recollection the parallelism of chemical research with that of every other search after truth; for it has been in overlooking this, that in chemistry false and vacillating theories have been advocated and a wrong route so often pursued. In mathematics the starting-point is not generalizations, but axioms, ultimate principles. In metaphysics, Descartes led the way of progress by analysing till he thought he could reach some ultimate elements beyond which it was impossible for him to go, then studying their force and power, and proceeding synthetically. The recognition of this method wrought the regeneration of science and philosophy.

On the other hand, look where Gerhardt's generalization of Williamson's generalization leads him, and legitimately too,—a fact which his logical spirit clearly discerned. He is led not to explain bodies according to their composition and inherent properties, but to think it necessary to restrict chemical science to the arrangement of bodies according to their decomposition, and to deny the possibility of our comprehending their molecular constitution. [3] Can such a view tend to the advancement of science? Would it not be only rational, in accepting this veto, to renounce chemical research altogether?

These reflections naturally lead to the inquiry after another theory more adequate to satisfy the just demands which can be made upon it. There is one which, as it is still supported by many distinguished chemists, cannot be passed over altogether unnoticed. It is that of the theory of certain combinates in organic chemistry which are to be viewed as analogous to, "playing the part of,"

---

[2] [Couper had also studied linguistics.—O.T.B.]

[3] [Williamson in 1851, on the other hand, suggested (see p. 70) that chemists should formulate "what we rationally suppose to be the arrangement of constituent atoms in a compound."—O.T.B.]

inorganic elements.   These are denominated radicals, and are supposed to be contained in all organic chemical products.

In addition to this, and also in connexion with it, there is a doctrine describing many combinates to be copulated, conjugated, by addition.

It is impossible here to enter upon any extensive criticism of this theory.   I can only remark that it is not merely an unprofitable figure of language, but is injurious to science, inasmuch as it tends to arrest scientific inquiry by adopting the notion that these quasi elements contain some unknown and ultimate power which it is impossible to explain.   It stifles inquiry at the very point where an explanation is demanded, by putting the seal of elements, of ultimate powers, on bodies which are known to be anything but this.

Science demands the strict adherence to a principle in direct contradiction to this view.   That first principle, without which research cannot advance a step, dare not be ignored; namely, that a whole is simply a derivative of its parts.   As a consequence of this, it follows that it is absolutely necessary to scientific unity and research to consider these bodies as entirely derivative, and as containing no secret ultimate power whatever, and that the properties which these so-called quasi elements possess are a direct consequence of the properties of the individual elements of which they are made up.

Nor is the doctrine of bodies being "conjugated by addition" a whit in advance of that which I have just been considering.   This doctrine adopts the simple expedient of dividing certain combinates, if possible, into two imaginary parts, of which one or both are bodies already known.   Then it tells us that these two parts are found united in this body.   But how they are united, or what force binds them together, it does not inquire.   Is this explication arbitrary? Is it instructive?   Is it science?

I may now be permitted to submit a few considerations relative to a more rational theory of chemical combination.

As everything depends upon the method of research employed, it will in the first place be necessary to find one that may be relied upon.   If the method is good, and conscientiously carried out, stable and satisfactory results may be expected.   If, on the contrary, it is vicious, we can only expect a corresponding issue.   A satisfactory method is, however, not difficult to find, nor is it difficult in its application.

The principle which ought to guide all research is in every case the same.   It is that of analysing till it is impossible to reach more simple elements, and of studying these elements in all their properties and powers. When all the properties and powers of the individual elements are known, then it will be possible to know the constitution of the combinates which their synthesis produces. It is necessary therefore in chemical research, in order to ascertain the various qualities and functions of the different elements,—

1. To consider the whole of chemistry as one.

2. To take into consideration every known combinate, and to study the character, functions, and properties displayed by each element for itself, in each of these combinates in all their different conditions and aspects. It is by a comparison of the different bodies among themselves that we are able to trace the part that is performed by each element separately.

3. To trace the general principles common to all the elements, noting the special properties of each.

This method is essentially different from that where one class of bodies is chosen as a point for the restriction of our views of the properties of the others—where only the qualities found in the first are to be measured out to the rest.

I shall now proceed to inquire how its more thorough application tends to the development of a rational chemical theory.

It has been found that there is one leading feature, one inherent property, common to all the elements. It has been denominated chemical affinity. It is discovered under two aspects:—(1) affinity of kind; (2) affinity of degree.

Affinity of kind is the special affinities manifested among the elements, the one for the other, etc., as carbon for oxygen, for chlorine, for hydrogen, etc.

Affinity of degree is the grades, or also limits of combination, which the elements display. For instance, C^2O^2 and C^2O^4 are the degrees of affinity of carbon for oxygen.[4] C^2O^2 may be called the first degree, and C^2O^4 may be termed the second degree, and, as a higher degree than this is not known for carbon, its ultimate affinity or combining limit. Affinity of degree in an element may have only one grade. It may have, however, and generally has more than one. Here then is an inherent property to all elements, by the removal of which the chemical character of an element will be destroyed, and by virtue of which an element finds its place marked out in a complex body.

It is such a property that is required to form the base of a system.

---

[4] [C=6 is here used, mainly because his readers were more used to it. On page 146 he explains why he prefers C=12 and utilizes the latter value for the rest of the paper.—O.T.B.]

Nor would its suitableness for this purpose be affected by the discovery that the elements are themselves composite bodies, which view the chemist is perhaps not unwarranted to adopt. For, in such a case, the necessity would doubtless still be found to exist of adopting the principle of affinity, or something at least equivalent to it, as the basis of the explanation of chemical combinates. In applying this method, I propose at present to consider the single element carbon. This body is found to have two highly distinguishing characteristics:—

1. It combines with equal numbers of hydrogen, chlorine, oxygen, sulphur, etc.

2. It enters into chemical union with itself.

These two properties, in my opinion, explain all that is characteristic of organic chemistry. This will be rendered apparent as I advance.

This second property is, so far as I am aware, here signalized for the first time. Evidence as to its being a property of carbon may therefore be required.

It will be found in the following:—What is the link which binds together bodies composed of 4, 6, 8, 10, 12, etc., equivalents of carbon, and as many equivalents of hydrogen, oxygen, etc.? In these you may remove perhaps all the hydrogen or oxygen, and substitute so many equivalents of chlorine, etc. It is then the carbon that is united to carbon. Further, that it is not the hydrogen that is the binding element in these combinates is evident; thus—

$$C^2 \begin{matrix} H \\ H \\ H \\ H \end{matrix} \qquad C^2 \left. \begin{matrix} O \\ O \\ O \\ O \end{matrix} \right\} \quad \text{and} \quad C^2 \begin{matrix} Cl \\ Cl \\ Cl \\ Cl \end{matrix}$$

Here the whole four of hydrogen are not bound by a mutual affinity; for each element of hydrogen can be substituted for one of chlorine in regular series, beginning with the first and ending with the last. The atoms of oxygen are, on the contrary, united in pairs (which will be more fully developed hereafter), and only for two atoms of oxygen two of chlorine can be substituted; thus—

$$C^2 \left. \begin{matrix} O \\ O \\ O \\ O \end{matrix} \right\} \qquad C^2 \left. \begin{matrix} Cl \\ Cl \\ O \\ O \end{matrix} \right\} \qquad C^2 \begin{matrix} Cl \\ Cl \\ Cl \\ Cl \end{matrix}$$

In the same manner, with bodies that contain multiples of C^2 united to hydrogen, etc.

Take the inverse of this. If the four atoms of hydrogen were bound together, we could evidently expect to form such bodies as

$$H^4 \begin{matrix} Cl \\ Cl \\ Cl \\ Cl \end{matrix} \qquad H^4 \begin{matrix} Br \\ Cl \\ Cl \\ Cl \end{matrix} \qquad H^4 \begin{matrix} Br \\ Br \\ Cl \\ Cl \end{matrix} \quad \text{and} \quad H^4 \begin{matrix} Br \\ Br \\ Br \\ Cl \end{matrix}$$

or for bodies like C^4H^4, C^6H^6, C^8H^8, one would naturally expect to find the carbon substituted for chlorine, and find bodies like $H^4{}^{Cl^2}_{Cl^2}$, H^6Cl^6, H^8Cl^8, etc.[5]

These bodies are not only unknown, but the whole history of hydrogen might be investigated and not a single instance be found to favour the opinion that it has any affinity for itself when in union with another element.

Now, on the other hand, carbon remains chemically united to carbon, while perhaps 8 equivalents of hydrogen are exchanged for 8 equivalents of chlorine, as in naphthaline. Analogous to this is the conversion of alcohol, $C^4{}^{O\cdots OH}_{H^5}$, and the hydrocarbide C^4H^6 into C^4Cl^6. All the countless instances of substitution of chlorine, etc., tend in the same direction. They prove beyond doubt that carbon enters into chemical union with carbon, and that in the most stable manner. This affinity, one of the strongest that carbon displays, is perhaps only inferior to that which it possesses for oxygen.

Another feature in the affinity of carbon is, that it combines by degrees of two; thus, C^2O^2 and C^2O^4, C^4H^4 and C^4H^6, C^6H^6 and C^6H^8, C^8H^8 and C^8H^{10}, etc.: from these last it is especially evident that two is the combining grade of carbon. It becomes still more apparent when we compare the bodies C^4H^4 and C^4H^5Cl, that is, $C^4H \left.\begin{matrix} Cl \\ H^4 \end{matrix}\right\}$ etc. Many such proofs might be added, while, on the other hand, there are no instances contradictory of this point. Hence the circumstance that it must ever remain impossible to isolate a combinate of the form C^2H^3 or C^4H^5, etc.

Carbon having only two grades of combination of two atoms each, a fact which is easily traced throughout all organic chemistry, this inherent property of the element may legitimately furnish two grand types for all its combinates.

The first type[6] will be nC^2M^4.

---

[5] Cl^2 is misprinted "C^2" in the original. See the French paper.

[6] [See p. 133, footnote 3.—O.T.B.]

The second type will be $nC^2M^4—mM^2$.[7]

As examples belonging to the first type, may be mentioned the alcohols of the æthylic form, their æthers, the fatty acids, etc.

Thus methylic alcohol has the formula $C^2\overset{\cdots O\cdots OH}{\underset{\cdots H^3}{}}$,

and æthylic alcohol,
$$C^2\overset{\cdots O\cdots OH}{\underset{\cdots H^2}{}}$$
$$\vdots$$
$$C^2\cdots H^3$$

In these instances it will be observed, that for each double atom of carbon the combining power is (4) four, which is the ultimate limit of combination for carbon in all bodies yet produced.

In the latter instance it is apparent, inasmuch as if the combining limit of two C^2s be each reduced by 3 in hydrogen or oxygen, there still remains a combining power of *one* to each of the two C^2s which each expends in uniting with the other; therefore
$$\begin{matrix} C^2\cdots H^3 \\ \vdots \\ C^2\cdots H^3 \end{matrix}$$
, or, what

is the same thing,
$$C^2\overset{\cdots O\cdots OH}{\underset{\cdots H^2}{}}$$
$$\vdots$$
$$C^2\cdots H^3$$
belongs to the type nC^2M^4.

Again, the inherent properties of the elements may be viewed as dividing bodies into primary, secondary, tertiary, and so on, combinates. These may be termed so many orders of complicity. Thus C^4H^6 is a primary combinate, or it belongs to the first order of complicity; but $C^4\overset{\cdots O\cdots OH}{\underset{\cdots H^5}{}}$ is a secondary combinate, or belongs to the second order of complicity. C^2O^2 and C^2O^4 are primary, while C^2O^4, $2OH$ and C^2O^4, $2OKa$ are secondary.

A primary combinate is then nC^2 united to nM^4 or to $nM^4—mM^2$ in such a manner that the combining energy of the complement (nM^4, etc.) either *potentially or actually* does not extend beyond nC^2.

A secondary combinate is one in which the combining energy of the complement is not all expended upon nC^2, but is extended further to one or more elements.

On the same principle there are tertiary combinates, etc.

These orders of complicity ought in reality to be subdivided. This, however, I do not think it necessary for the present to enter upon. It will now be understood why an alcohol belongs to the

---

[7] Misprinted "mM" in the original.

type nC^2M^4, and on the same principle why a free æther belongs to

the same type, thus
$$C^2 \cdots O \cdots \cdots O \cdots C^2$$
$$\vdots \quad \cdots H^2 \quad H^2 \cdots \quad \vdots$$
$$\vdots \qquad \qquad \vdots$$
$$C^2 \cdots H^3 \quad H^3 \cdots C^2$$
,[8] while they are at the same

time secondary combinates.

A secondary combinate, that is to say, a body belonging to the second order of complicity, is, as will be understood from the principle which forms the ground of the rational theory, a direct consequence of an inherent property of one or more of the elements which form the complement to the carbon.

In the instance before us, it is a certain property of the oxygen which is the cause of the secondary combinate. This property is the affinity which one atom of oxygen in combination always exerts towards another atom of oxygen likewise in combination.

This affinity is modified by the electric position of the element to which the respective atoms of oxygen are bound. From this property results the fact, that in organic combinates the atoms of oxygen are always found double.

For instance, the combining limit of oxygen being two, when two

molecules of
$$C^2 \cdots O \cdots$$
$$\vdots \quad \cdots H^2$$
$$\vdots$$
$$C^2 \cdots H^3$$
are set at liberty, the free affinities of the oxy-

gen instantly produce the union of these molecules. The cause of the union of two molecules of C^2H^3 has been already remarked. In the two cases, the causes of the union of the respective molecules are in so far different, that the one is the result of a property of the carbon, while the other is the result of a property of the oxygen.

The view here adopted of the nature of oxygen is, I am convinced, alone in conformity with the reactions where the properties of this body develope themselves.

The vapour of anhydrous sulphuric acid, for instance, is conducted into anhydrous æther.[9] The following will then

be the reaction:—
$$S^2 \begin{array}{c} O \\ \diagup \\ \cdots O \\ \cdots O^2 \\ \diagdown \\ O^2 \end{array}$$
entering into communication with

---

[8] The vertical dotted line between these two "C^2's" is omitted in the original.

[9] [The reaction is that of SO_3 with $C_2H_5OC_2H_5$. The argument shows the strong influence of electrochemical doctrines.—O.T.B.]

$C^4 \overset{\cdots O \cdots}{\underset{\cdots H^5}{}} \overset{O \cdots}{\underset{H^5 \cdots}{}} C^4$, the two atoms of the oxygen of the sulphuric acid
and the two atoms of the oxygen of the æther (now in presence of
each other) being in different (perhaps different electric) conditions,
mutually loosen their former affinities and reunite themselves to the
(electrically?) different atoms of oxygen of these respective combinates.

The same principle may naturally be expected to display itself
with regard to acids and bases. The oxygen of an acid unites itself
to the (electrically?) different oxygen of water. The oxygen of a
base on the same principle has an affinity for the electrically different oxygen of water.

It will be observed—

1. That the oxygen of the water of an acid can only be expelled
by that of a base and *vice versa*.

2. It is to be remarked that *it is not* the metal of a base which exchanges places with the hydrogen of the hydrate of an acid; for if
that were the case, the affinity of the oxygen of the metal, and also
of the acid, *would be greater for the oxygen of the water* than the affinity
of the hydrogen for that same oxygen. But this is not so. The
very opposite is the truth. If one atom of hydrogen be withdrawn
from the hydrate of an acid or from *the hydrate of an oxide, it is
universally accompanied by an atom of oxygen*. It is evident, then, that
the affinity between *the positive and negative atoms of oxygen is less than
that which attaches these atoms to the element with which they form a
primary combinate.*

A consequence of this truth is, that it is impossible to double the
equivalent of oxygen, if the chemical equivalents are to be understood as not being in direct contradiction to any chemical truth or
essential feature in the properties of an element. Carbon differs
entirely in this respect from oxygen.

There is no reaction found where it is known that C^2 is divided
into two parts. It is only consequent therefore to write, with Gerhardt, C^2 simply as C, it being then understood that the equivalent
of carbon is (12) twelve.

This value of the atom will be adopted in the following part of
this paper.

Sulphur, selenium, etc., being bodies displaying properties
similar, not to carbon, but to oxygen, it will be necessary to retain
the equivalent value that has generally been assigned to them.

I have now shown how ordinary alcohol, $C^2H^6O^2$, common
æther, and the hydrocarbide, C^2H^6, belong to the type nCM^4.
The phenomena which necessitate this view of the constitution of

these bodies have a like consequence in regard to the other alcohols, glycols, acids, and æthers of this series.

Propyle alcohol is
$$C\overset{\cdots O\cdots OH}{\underset{\cdots H^2}{\vdots}}$$
$$C\cdots H^2$$
$$C\cdots H^3$$
, where it will be seen that the

atom of carbon situated between the two others, on account of being chemically united to these, is reduced to the combining power of two for hydrogen, oxygen, etc. One combining power is given up to the carbon upon the one side, and a second to the carbon upon the other.

It will be observed also that the primary combinates ought in rigour to be themselves enumerated in an inverse order. The type nCM^4 becomes then in reality the type CM^4. This enumeration, however, does not appear to possess any great practical utility, and it is perhaps preferable simply to denote it in an indefinite manner by adding "n" to the true type CM^4.

In like manner the butyle alcohol is to be viewed as
$$C\overset{\cdots O\cdots OH}{\underset{\cdots H^2}{\vdots}}$$
$$C\cdots H^2$$
$$C\cdots H^2$$
$$C\cdots H^3$$
,

and so on throughout all the series of these alcohols. The constitution of the æthers will be evident:
$$C\overset{\cdots O\cdots\cdots\cdots O\cdots}{\underset{\cdots H^2\quad H^2\cdots}{\vdots}}C$$
$$C\cdots H^2\quad H^3\cdots C \quad {}^{10}$$
$$C\cdots H^2$$
$$C\cdots H^3$$
represents

the mixed butylic-ethylic æther.

Formic acid is represented by the form
$$C\overset{O\cdots OH}{\underset{H}{\overset{\cdots O^2}{\vdots}}}$$
; acetic acid

---

[10] The vertical dotted lines between the two "C's" is omitted in the original.

in like manner,
$$\begin{array}{l} C\cdots O\cdots OH \\ \vdots \cdots O^2 \\ C\cdots H^3 \end{array}$$
Propionic acid is
$$\begin{array}{l} C\cdots O\cdots OH \\ \vdots \cdots O^2 \\ C\cdots H^2 \\ \vdots \\ C\cdots H^3 \end{array}$$
The

constitution of glycol may be represented as follows:—
$$\begin{array}{l} C\cdots O\cdots OH \\ \vdots \cdots H^2 \\ \vdots \cdots H^2 \\ C\cdots O\cdots OH. \end{array}$$

In like manner as to the acids of these glycols; oxalic acid, for instance, may be represented as
$$\begin{array}{l} C\cdots O\cdots OH \\ \vdots \cdots O^2 \\ \vdots \cdots O^2 \\ C\cdots O\cdots OH \end{array}$$

Respecting these acids, it may perhaps be allowable to suggest the possibility of the molecule having two poles, and that especially the atom of oxygen situated at one or perhaps both, and near to two atoms of oxygen bound together, and forming no secondary combinate, may be in a state presenting great affinity for basic oxygen. Analogy with electric poles may perhaps demand the opinion that all the negative oxygen be situated upon one side of the molecule. It will in that case be preferable to represent the oxalic acid as

$$\begin{array}{l} C\cdots O^2 \\ \vdots \cdots O^2 \\ C\cdots O\cdots OH \\ O\cdots OH \end{array}$$
Be that as it may, however, the rational method of

investigation proves it to be a law, that in acids of the type nCM^4 the presence of two atoms of oxygen bound together so as to form only a primary part of the same molecule, and situated close to the negative oxygen, is necessary to the calling forth or production of this negative state.[11]

This is a particular instance, but it moreover *shows generally how the electro-positive or the electro-negative value of the elements mutually modify and condition the electro-positive or electro-negative value* of each other when in combination.

This law is different from the electric hypothesis which chemists

---

[11] [Couper is realizing the difference between the two oxygens in a carboxylic acid. A carbonyl group (C=O) must be adjacent to a group —OH in order to bring out the acidic character of the latter.—O.T.B.]

have formerly defended, but which never could be traced through-out a thoroughgoing application of their views to organic chemistry.

The law here distinctly enounced coincides exactly with, and is rendered apparent by the application of the theory of chemical combination which I support.

But to return.   Glycerine is

```
        O····OH                          H
       .·                               .·
    C····O····OH                     C····O····OH
    :    `.                          :    `.
    :     H                          :     O····OH
    :            , and glyceric acid :
    C····H²                          C····H²
    :                                :
    C····H²                          C····O²
     `····O····OH                     `····O····OH
```

Glucose has been perhaps too little investigated to afford data sufficient to determine definitely its formula.   Taking, however, mucic and saccharic acids as starting-points, these bodies may be meanwhile represented as shown on the next page.

It will thus be seen that these combinates all belong to type nCM^4.

Many others might be added.[12]   For instance, tartaric acid:—

```
    C····O····OH  ⎤                              ⎧ C····O····OH
     `····O²      ⎥                              ⎪  `····O²
                  ⎥                              ⎪ C····H
    C····H        ⎥   And the bibasic acid       ⎪ :  `····O²  tartrelic
     `····O····OH ⎥   produced from it by    ⎬  ⎨ C           acid.
                  ⎥   the   action   of  heat     ⎪  `····H
    C····O····OH  ⎥   will be perhaps            ⎪
     `····H ¹³    ⎥                              ⎪ C····O²
                  ⎥                              ⎩  `····O····OH
    C····O²       ⎥
     `····O····OH ⎦
```

It is my intention to consider, in a future communication, the second type, and to apply my views to the cyanogen combinates, etc.

---

[12] [In the French version (*Ann. Chim.* (3), *53*, 489 (1858)) Couper adds the following cyclic formula for cyanuric acid, seven years before Kekulé proposed the cyclic benzene formula:

```
        HO—O—Az—C—AzO—OH
              |        \
              C         \
               \        ⎧ C
                \   Az ⎨
                      ⎩ O—OH            —O.T.B.]
```

[13] A horizontal dotted line is erroneously printed here in the original.

the acids.   Glucose.

---

14 This "OH" is omitted in the original.

15 The oblique dotted line here is omitted in the original.

16 The vertical dotted line between the "C's" is omitted in the original.

8

Jacobus Henricus van't Hoff

A Suggestion Looking to the Extension into Space of the Structural Formulas at Present Used in Chemistry.   And a Note upon the Relation between the Optical Activity and the Chemical Constitution of Organic Compounds

[From *Foundations of Stereochemistry.   Memoirs by Pasteur, van't Hoff, le Bel and Wislicenus*, translated and edited by George M. Richardson, New York, American Book Company, 1901, 37–46 ; translation of "Sur les formules de structure dans l'espace," *Archives Néerlandaises des Sciences Exactes et Naturelles*, 9, 445–454 (1874).

This paper was the French translation of a printed pamphlet with small circulation which van't Hoff had published a few months earlier under the title *Voorstel tot uitbreiding der tegenwoordig in de scheikunde gebruikte structuurformules in de ruimte, benevens een daarmee samenhangende opmerking omtrent het verband tusschen optisch actief vermogen en chemische constitutie van organische verbindingen* (Utrecht, J. Greven, 1874).]

I desire to introduce some remarks which may lead to discussion and hope to avail myself of the discussion to give to my ideas more definiteness and breadth.   Since the starting point for the following communication is found in the chemistry of the carbon compounds, I shall for the present do nothing more than state the points having reference to it.

It appears more and more that the present constitutional formulas are incapable of explaining certain cases of isomerism; the reason for this is perhaps the fact that we need a more definite statement about the actual positions of the atoms.

If we suppose that the atoms lie in a plane, as for example with isobutyl alcohol (Figure I.)[1] where the four affinities are represented by four lines in this plane occupying two directions

---

[1] [The figures appear at the end of the paper.—O.T.B.]

perpendicular to one another, then methane (CH_4) (to start with the simplest case) will give the following isomeric modifications (the different hydrogen atoms being replaced one after the other by univalent groups R' R'' etc.):

One for	CH_3R'	and for	CHR'_3
Two for	$CH_2R'_2$ (Figures II. and III.), for		
	$CH_2R'R''$,	and for	CHR'_2R''
Three for	$CHR'R''R'''$	and for	$CR'R''R'''R''''$
	(Figures IV., V. and VI.;)		

numbers that are clearly greater than the numbers actually known thus far.

The theory is brought into accord with the facts if we consider the affinities of the carbon atom directed toward the corners of a tetrahedron of which the carbon atom itself occupies the center.

The number of isomers is then reduced and will be as follows:

One for	CH_3R',	$CH_2R'_2$,	$CH_2R'R''$,	CHR'_3,
and	CHR'_2R''		but	
Two for	$CHR'R''R'''$		or more generally for	
	$CR'R''R'''R''''$			

If one imagines himself in the line $R'R'''$ in Figures VII. and VIII. with head toward R' and looking toward the line $R''R'''$ then R'' may be on the right (Figure VII.) or on the left (Figure VIII.) of the observer; in other words: *When the four affinities of the carbon atom are satisfied by four univalent groups differing among themselves, two and not more than two different tetrahedrons are obtained, one of which is the reflected image of the other, they cannot be superposed; that is, we have here to deal with two structural formulas isomeric in space.* According to this hypothesis the combination $CR'R''R'''R''''$ presents a condition not presented by the combinations $CR'_2R''R'''$, CR'_3R'' or CR'_4, a condition not expressed by the ordinary mode of representation. According to the present mode there would be between $CR'R''R'''R''''$ and $CR'_2R''R'''$ a difference quite as great as between $CR'_2R''R'''$ and CR'_3R'', or between CR'_3R'' and CR'_4.

Submitting the first result of this hypothesis to the control of facts, I believe that it has been thoroughly established that some combinations which contain a carbon atom combined with four different univalent groups (such carbon atoms will henceforth be called asymmetric carbon atoms) present some anomalies in relation to isomerism and other characteristics which are not indicated by the constitutional formulas thus far used.

JACOBUS HENRICUS VAN'T HOFF (1852–
1911). From *Jacobus Henricus van't Hoff, Sein
Leben und Wirken* by Ernst Cohen.   Leipzig, 1912.
Courtesy of the publisher, Akademische Verlagsgesellschaft, Frankfurt/Main.

FIRST PART. I. RELATION BETWEEN THE ASYMMETRIC CARBON AND THE PROPERTY OF OPTICAL ACTIVITY.

(*a*) *All of the compounds of carbon which in solution rotate the plane of polarized light possess an asymmetric carbon atom.*

In order to convince oneself of the justice of these remarks it is necessary to run through the following list of optically active compounds in the formula of which the asymmetric carbon is indicated by **C**:

Ethylidene lactic acid, CH_3**C**.H. OH. COOH.

Aspartic acid,   COOH **C**.H. NH_2 (CH_2 COOH).

Asparagine,   COOH **C**.H. NH_2. (CH_2 $CONH_2$).

Malic acid,   COOH **C**. OH. H. (CH_2 COOH).

Glutaric acid [Itamalic acid]

        CH_2OH **C**.H. COOH. (CH_2 COOH).

Tartaric acid,   COOH **C**.H. OH.   **C**.H. OH. COOH.

Dextrose, Lævulose, Galactose, Maltose.

Sorbin, Eucalyn, etc., CH_2 OH. **C**.H. OH. ($C_4H_7O_4$)

Mannite, Quercite, Pinite: ($C_4H_9O_4$). **C**. H. OH. CH_2OH.

Cane sugar, milk sugar, Melezitose, Melitose, Parasacchrose, and Trehalose; Starch, Inuline, Glycogen, Dextrine, and Arabin all contain the asymmetric carbon atom that was present in the previous compounds inasmuch as they are compound ethers of the previous compounds.

Camphor, according to KEKULÉ (Figure XII.).

Borneol, according to the same (Figure XIII.).

Camphoric acid, according to the same.

       COOH **C**H ($C_8H_{14}O$.).

Terpinolene which apparently has the structure shown in Figure XIV. and Menthol which perhaps has the structure shown in Figure XV.

Concerning the active alkaloids, albumens, etc., too little is as yet known of their structure to permit of any conclusion being reached in regard to the relation between their structure and the rotatory power.

The sole definite exception to this rule that I have been able to find is the active propyl alcohol of Chancell, but, according to a private communication of Henniger, this relatively small rotatory power is due to the presence of an impurity.

(*b*) *The derivatives of optically active compounds lose their rotatory power when the asymmetry of all of the carbon atoms disappears; in the contrary case they do not usually lose this power.*

A few examples will be sufficient here:

Inactive malonic, fumaric, and maleïc acids from the active malic acid; inactive succinic and tartronic acids from the active tartaric acid; inactive cymene from active camphor, etc.

In the contrary case there are,

Active malic acid from active tartaric acid;

Active tartaric acid from active lactose;

Active glucose from active glucosides;

Active nitro mannite from active mannite;

Active camphoric acid and Borneol from active camphor;

Active salts and esters from active acids, etc.

(*c*) *If one makes a list of compounds which contain an asymmetric carbon atom it is then seen that in many cases the converse of* (*a*) *is not true, that is, not every compound with such an atom has an influence upon polarized light.*

This may be ascribed to three causes:

1. The compounds consist of an inactive mixture of two isomers with equal but opposite optical power, which owing to their close agreement in all other properties can be separated with great difficulty, and which have not up to the present been separated.

2. The study of the rotatory power has been imperfect, either on account of the slight solubility of the compounds or on account of the slight specific rotatory power of many compounds, as for example, in the case of mannite.

3. The asymmetric carbon atom may not in itself be sufficient to cause optical activity, the latter may not depend solely upon the mutual diversity of the groups which are in combination with the carbon atom, but may also be dependent upon their character.

However the case may be, the facts noted indicate a probable relation between constitution and active power which may be made use of in the following cases when more convincing arguments fail:

1. A compound which rotates the plane of polarized light probably possesses an asymmetric carbon atom; which gives a means of choosing between possible structures in the case of compounds where the structure is not completely determined.

For example, active amyl alcohol with an asymmetric carbon atom can have only the formula.

$$\begin{matrix} CH_3 \\ C_2H_5 \end{matrix} \; CH. \; CH_2 OH$$

a formula which has also been suggested by Erlenmeyer but upon altogether different grounds.

2. A compound which up to the present has shown no physical isomers acting upon polarized light in all probability contains no asymmetric carbon atom; this fact also may be of service in choosing

between possible structural formulas; as, for example, citric acid, which on account of its transformation into aconitic and tricarballylic acids must have one of the two formulas:

$$
\begin{array}{ccc}
\text{C.H. OH. COOH} & & \text{CH}_2\text{ COOH} \\
| & & | \\
\text{CH. COOH} & \text{or} & \text{C. OH. COOH} \\
| & & | \\
\text{CH}_2\text{ COOH} & & \text{CH}_2\text{ COOH}
\end{array}
$$

Its inactivity gives preference to the second formula; the first, however, contains an asymmetric carbon atom, for which reason I hope to be able to produce the acid named by following the method of Frankland and Duppa from oxalic acid and iodo acetic acid esters by the aid of zinc.

3. Finally the limits of the rotatory power can be stated with some measure of probability, that is to say, the simplest combinations which will show active power can be indicated; for example, the simplest active monatomic alcohol will be:

$$\text{CH}_3.\ \text{C. H. OH. CH}_2\ \text{CH}_3.$$

The simplest active monobasic acid:

$$\text{CH}_3.\ \text{C. H. COOH. CH}_2\ \text{CH}_3.$$

The simplest active diatomic alcohol:

$$\text{CH}_3\ \text{CHOH CH}_2\ \text{OH}.$$

The simplest active saturated hydrocarbon:

$$
\begin{array}{l}
\text{CH}_3 \\
\text{C}_2\text{H}_5
\end{array}\ \text{CH. C}_3\ \text{H}_7
$$

The simplest active aromatic hydrocarbon:

$$
\begin{array}{l}
\text{CH}_3 \\
\text{C}_2\text{H}_5
\end{array}\ \text{CH. C}_6\text{H}_5\ \text{etc.}
$$

At the same time it is probable that some series will be excluded from active power, as for example:

The normal hydrocarbons	$\text{CH}_3\ (\text{CH}_2)_n\ \text{CH}_3$
The normal alcohols	$\text{CH}_3\ (\text{CH}_2)_n\ \text{CH}_2\text{OH}$
The normal acids	$\text{CH}_3\ (\text{CH}_2)_n\ \text{COOH}$ etc.

It is more noteworthy that in consequence of the assumptions made, the compound CH Br Cl I can probably be split up into two isomers which will act upon polarized light.[2]

---

[2] [Van't Hoff is here proposing an optically active compound containing only a single carbon atom. Such a compound was not obtained until Pope and Read in 1914 synthesized and resolved $\text{CHIClSO}_3\text{H}$ (*J. Chem. Soc., 105*, 811 (1914)).]

II. RELATION BETWEEN THE ASYMMETRIC CARBON ATOM AND THE NUMBER OF ISOMERS. Since perhaps the asymmetric carbon atom does not cause all compounds in which it is present to be optically active, it ought, according to the fundamental hypothesis, to cause an isomerism which will show itself in one way or another; in consequence the number of isomers foreseen by the present structural formulas will be doubled by the presence of a single asymmetric carbon atom, and is further increased by the presence of several.

I believe that there are compounds which show this apparent anomaly which Wislicenus has stamped with the name of geometric isomerism, at the same time he pointed to the unsatisfactory nature of the present ideas without in any way proposing an hypothesis which would be more logical.

Among these may be mentioned the ethylidene lactic acid which has one asymmetric carbon atom;

Tartaric acid, dibrom- and isodibrom-succinic acid, citra-, ita- and mesa-brompyrotartaric acid, citra-, ita-. and mesa-malic acid, mannite and its isomers, dextrose and its isomers, perhaps also terpinolene, the sugars, etc., with their isomers, in all of which several asymmetric carbon atoms act together to increase the number of the isomers.

SECOND PART. Thus far we have considered the influence of the hypothesis upon compounds in which the carbon atoms are united by a single affinity only, (leaving out some aromatic bodies); there remains now to be considered:

The influence of the new hypothesis upon compounds containing doubly linked carbon atoms. Double linking is represented by two tetrahedrons with one edge in common (Figure IX.) in which A and B represent the union of the two carbon atoms, and R′ R″ R‴ R⁗ represent the univalent groups which saturate the remaining free affinities of the carbon atoms.

If R′ R″ R‴ R⁗ all represent the same group, then but one form is conceivable, and the same is true if R′ and R″ or R‴ and R⁗ are identical, *but if R′ differs from R″ and at the same time R‴ differs from R⁗, which does not preclude R′ and R″, R″ and R⁗ from being equal, then two figures become possible shown in Figures IX. and X., which differ from one another in regard to the positions of R′ and R″ with respect to R‴ and R⁗. The dissimilarity of these figures, which are limited to two, indicates a case of isomerism not shown by the ordinary formulas.*

Turning to the facts, I believe that I have met with such cases among organic compounds.

1. Maleïc and fumaric acids. All explanations of the isomerism between these have made shipwreck (I count here also the assump-

tion of a bivalent carbon atom since this can exist alone in the case of carbon monoxide and the carbylamines for evident reasons, without doubling of the molecule); as a matter of fact these acids realize the conditions outlined above: *Two doubly linked carbon atoms each carrying two unlike univalent groups, H and COOH.*

2. Brom and isobrom maleïc acid. The explanation of the isomerism here is entirely the same as before, one has only to replace an H in the fumaric and maleïc acid by a Br.

3. Citra-, ita- and mesaconic acids. With the adoption of

$$CH_3 \ CH \ COOH \ CH_2 \ COOH$$

for pyrotartaric acid there remains for the acids mentioned only the formulas

$$CH_2{=}C. \ COOH. \ CH_2 \ COOH$$
$$CH_3 \ C \ COOH{=}CH. \ COOH$$

and if the latter does not contain two isomers (probably ita- and citraconic acids) in accordance with my hypothesis, no plausible explanation can be given.

4. Solid and liquid crotonic acids. The constitution of the solid crotonic acid according to Kekulé is without doubt

$$CH_3 \ CH{=}CH \ COOH$$

for the liquid crotonic acid there remains therefore (thus it is held) only the formula

$$CH_2{=}CH \ CH_2 \ COOH$$

to explain their lack of identity.

But if we take into consideration the following facts with regard to this acid:

(*a*) Fused with KOH it gives, according to M. Hemilian, acetic acid only.

(*b*) Oxidizing agents, according to the same authority, convert it into acetic and oxalic acids, and indirectly from the oxalic acid into carbonic acid.

(*c*) At 170°–180°, also according to Hemilian, it goes over into the solid crotonic acid. Thus there is nothing in favor of the formula $CH_2{=}CH \ CH_2 \ COOH$ and everything in favor of the isomer $CH_3 \ CH{=}CH \ COOH$, exactly like fumaric and maleïc acids. The formula $CH_3 \ CH{=}CH \ COOH$ really satisfies the conditions exacted by my hypothesis for the possibility of two isomers: two doubly linked carbon atoms, the free affinities of each of which are saturated by two unlike univalent groups, in this case H and CH_3, H and COOH.

Geuther's chlorcrotonic acid and chlorisocrotonic acid, the isomerism of which has hitherto been expressed by the formulas

$$CH_2\!\!=\!\!CCl\ CH_2\ COOH$$
and $$CH_3\ CCl\!\!=\!\!CHCOOH,$$

according to Froelich give with nascent hydrogen the acids treated of under (4) whence the constitution of both becomes

$$CH_3\ CCl\!\!=\!\!CHCOOH$$

and this case of isomerism strengthens my hypothesis.

THIRD PART. There remain now to be treated carbon atoms which are united by a triple union as in acetylene; this combination is represented by two tetrahedrons with three summits in common or with one of their faces in common (Figure XI.). ACB is the triple union, R' and R" are the univalent groups which saturate the two remaining affinities of the carbon atoms. The new hypothesis does not in this case lead to any discordance with the views previously held.

In closing I wish to remark that

1. The new hypothesis leaves nothing unexplained that is clearly set forth by the previous conceptions.

2. Certain properties and isomers not explained by the usual theories receive some light from this point of view.

3. Finally my remarks about active compounds in solution, that is active molecules, are related to the views of Rammelsberg upon active crystals.

Extending the observations of Herschell and Pasteur, Rammelsberg maintains that the property of acting upon the plane of polarization in the solid state (that is the active condition of crystals with inactive molecules as well as the inactive condition of crystals with active molecules) coincides with the appearance of two crystal forms, one of which is the reflected image of the other.

It is evident that we have here to deal with an arrangement of the molecules in the active crystal altogether similar to the arrangement of the groups of atoms in the active molecule according to my hypothesis; an arrangement in which neither the crystal mentioned by Rammelsberg nor the active molecules, represented in a general way by Figures VII. and VIII., have a plane of symmetry.[3]

---

[3] [Van't Hoff's work would, in all likelihood, not have created too much attention had not Wislicenus chosen to champion the former's views. Wislicenus wrote a preface to the German edition of van't Hoff's *La Chimie dans l'Espace*, which he had asked his student, F. Hermann, to translate. This preface drew upon Wislicenus

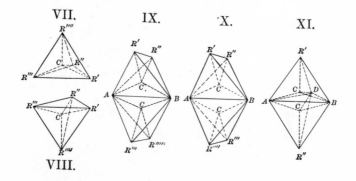

and van't Hoff the fury of Hermann Kolbe. "I would have ignored this work as I have done many others, had not a significant chemist taken it under his protection and recommended it as a worthy achievement.... To criticize this paper in any detail is impossible because the play of the imagination completely forsakes the solid ground of fact and is quite incomprehensible to the sober chemist." (H. Kolbe, *J. prakt. Chem.*, (2), *15*, 473 (1877). A more complete English translation of the Kolbe tirade appeared in G. W. Wheland, *Advanced Organic Chemistry*, 2nd Edition, New York, John Wiley & Sons, 1949, p. 132.)

Kolbe's attack on the use of the imagination in science led, in turn, to van't Hoff's exploration of the role of the imaginative faculty in the lives of great scientists. His inaugural address as professor of chemistry in Amsterdam dealt with this topic. (J. H. van't Hoff, *De Verbeeldingskracht in de Wetenschap*, Rotterdam, P. M. Bazendijk, 1878, pp. 4–24. Translated by O. T. Benfey, *J. chem. Educ.*, *37*, 467 (1960))—O.T.B.]

XII.   XIII.   XIV.   XV.

C_3H_7 C_3H_7 C_3H_7 C_3H_7
| | | |
CH   CH   CH   CH

H_2C CH_2 H_2C CH_2 H_2C CH H_2C CH_2

HC   CO   HC   CHOH   HC   CH H_2C CHOH

C   C   C   CH
| | | |
CH_3 CH_3 CH_3 CH_3

J. H. VAN'T HOFF.

Utrecht, Sept. 5, '74.

9

Joseph Achille le Bel

On the Relations Which Exist between the Atomic Formulas of Organic Compounds and the Rotatory Power of Their Solutions

[From *Foundations of Stereochemistry. Memoirs by Pasteur, van't Hoff, le Bel and Wislicenus*, translated and edited by George M. Richardson, New York, American Book Company, 1901, 49–59; translation of "Sur les relations qui existent entre les formules atomiques des corps organiques, et le pouvoir rotatoire de leurs dissolutions," *Bulletin de la Société Chimique de France*, [2], 22, 337–347 (1874).]

Up to the present time we do not possess any certain rule which enables us to foresee whether or not the solution of a substance has rotatory power. We know only that the derivatives of an active substance are in general also active; nevertheless we often see the rotatory power suddenly disappear in the most immediate derivatives, while in other cases it persists in very remote derivatives. By considerations, purely geometrical, I have been able to formulate a rule of a quite general character.

Before giving the reasoning which has led me to this law I shall give the facts upon which it rests, and then shall conclude with a discussion of the confirmation of the law offered by the present state of our chemical knowledge.

The labors of Pasteur and others have completely established the correlation which exists between molecular asymmetry and rotatory power. If the asymmetry exists only in the crystalline molecule, the crystal alone will be active; if, on the contrary, it belongs to the chemical molecule the solution will show rotatory power, and often the crystal also if the structure of the crystal allows us to perceive it, as in the case of the sulphate of strychnine and the alum of amylamine.

There are, moreover, mathematical demonstrations of the necessary existence of this correlation, which we may consider a perfectly ascertained fact.

In the reasoning which follows, we shall ignore the asymmetries which might arise from the arrangement in space possessed by the atoms and univalent radicals; but shall consider them as spheres or material points, which will be equal if the atoms or radicals are equal, and different if they are different. This restriction is justified by the fact, that, up to the present time, it has been possible to account for all the cases of isomerism observed without recourse to such arrangement, and the discussion at the end of the paper will show that the appearance of the rotatory power can be equally well foreseen without the aid of the hypothesis of which we have just spoken.

First General Principle. Let us consider a molecule of a chemical compound having the formula $M A_4$; M being a simple or complex radical combined with four univalent atoms A, capable of being replaced by substitution. Let us replace three of them by simple or complex univalent radicals differing from one another and from M; the body obtained will be asymmetric.

Indeed, the group of radicals R, R', R'', A when considered as material points differing among themselves form a structure which is enantiomorphous with its reflected image, and the residue, M, cannot re-establish the symmetry. In general then it may be stated that if a body is derived from the original type $M A_4$ by the substitution of three different atoms or radicals for A, its molecules will be asymmetric, and it will have rotatory power.

But there are two exceptional cases, distinct in character.

(1) If the molecular type has a plane of symmetry containing the four atoms A, the substitution of these by radicals (which we must consider as not capable of changing their position) can in no way alter the symmetry with respect to this plane, and in such cases the whole series of substitution products will be inactive.

(2) The last radical substituted[1] for A may be composed of the same atoms that compose all of the rest of the group into which it enters, and these two equal groups may have a neutralizing effect upon polarized light, or they may increase the activity; when the former is the case the body will be inactive. Now this arrangement may present itself in a derivative of an active asymmetric body where there is but slight difference in constitution, and later we shall see a remarkable instance of this.

Second General Principle. If in our fundamental type we substitute but two radicals R, R', it is possible to have symmetry or

---

[1] [Le Bel is proposing a molecule CABDA in which the last atom or group A is now replaced by the grouping CABD. The example of tartaric acid is discussed on page 164.—O.T.B.]

JOSEPH ACHILLE LE BEL (1847–1930). From
Proceedings of the Royal Society of London, Series A,
Vol. CXXX, 1931. Courtesy of the Royal Society
of London.

asymmetry according to the constitution of the original type $M A_4$. If this molecule originally had a plane of symmetry passing through the two atoms A which have been replaced by R and R′, this plane will remain a plane of symmetry after the substitution; the body obtained will then be inactive. Our knowledge of the constitution of certain simple types will enable us to assert, that certain bodies derived from them by two substitutions will be inactive.

Again, if it happens not only that a single substitution furnishes but one derivative, but also that two and even three substitutions give only one and the same chemical isomer,[2] we are obliged to admit that the four atoms A occupy the angles of a regular tetrahedron, whose planes of symmetry are identical with those of the whole molecule $M A_4$; in this case also no bisubstitution product can have rotatory power.

Application to the Saturated Bodies of the Fatty Series. All of the saturated bodies of the fatty series are derived from marsh gas, CH_4, by the replacement of the hydrogen by different radicals. Provided that the four atoms of hydrogen are not all in the same plane, a supposition upon which the very existence of active trisubstitution products is based, we are able to apply the first general principle and assert that the substitution of three different radicals will furnish active bodies. Thus, if in the constitutional formula of a substance, we find a carbon atom combined with three univalent radicals different from each other and from hydrogen, we ought to find it an active body.

Further[3] as marsh gas never furnishes more than one derivative by two and three substitutions we can apply to the derivatives formed by two substitutions the second general principle and assert that such derivatives are never active; thus if in a constitutional formula we see a carbon atom combined with two atoms of hydrogen or with two identical radicals, such a body ought not to show rotatory power.

Let us now pass in review the active bodies of the fatty series.

---

[2] [By *chemical* isomer, le Bel means isomers differing in characteristics other than their direction of rotation of polarized light. Those differing only in their effect on polarized light were often spoken of as *physical* isomers.—O.T.B.]

[3] [This paragraph, coupled with the next but one before it, clearly implies a regular tetrahedral structure for methane, a fact that has been denied by some. (Cf. A. Findlay, *A Hundred Years of Chemistry*, New York: Macmillan, 1938, p. 73. The author suggests that in van't Hoff's mind arose the idea of the tetrahedral carbon atom, in le Bel's the idea of the asymmetric carbon atom. In fact, each paper contains both ideas. Cf. also A. Sementsov, *American Scientist, 43,* 97 (1955).)—O.T.B.]

Lactic Group. Lactic acid is derived from marsh gas by the substitution of a part of the hydrogen by the three groups HO, COOH, and CH_3 differing from one another, for this acid has the formula

$$
\begin{array}{c}
H \\
| \\
CH_3\!-\!C\!-\!COOH \\
| \\
HO
\end{array}
$$

The central carbon atom is in this case one to which the first general principle can be applied; this body ought to be active.

Mr. Wislicenus has, in fact, recently announced that he has found an active acid in meat. This acid does not have, as has been believed, the constitution of the ethylene lactic acid; but it is according to this author a physical isomer of the ordinary lactic acid. Indeed one cannot see that the ethylene lactic acid can be active, for the carbons of the radical are each one combined with two atoms of hydrogen, as the formula shows: CH_2 OH CH_2 COOH. We see also that the propylene glycol and the iodopropionic acid which are derived from the active lactic acid will preserve the rotatory power, but it will not be the same with the glycerine which one can derive from it, for in that case the central carbon atom is united with the two equal radicals CH_2 OH.

Malic Group. Malic acid presents a character altogether analogous; its formula places its rotatory character in evidence.

$$
\begin{array}{c}
H \\
| \\
COOH\!-\!CH_2\!-\!C\!-\!COOH \\
| \\
O\,H
\end{array}
$$

It is the same for asparagine which is derived from malic acid by the substitution of NH_2 for two of the hydroxyls of the latter. Indeed, aspartic acid which is still active contains a single NH_2 in the place of the central hydroxyl.

If, on the other hand, we replace this hydroxyl by H, we form succinic acid, which, like the ethylene lactic acid, is inactive.

Tartaric Group. Tartaric acid has the formula:

$$
\begin{array}{c}
\left[\begin{array}{c}
H \\
| \\
COOH\!-\!C \\
| \\
HO
\end{array}\right.
\begin{array}{c}
H \\
| \\
C\!-\!COOH \\
| \\
OH
\end{array}
\end{array}
$$

It may be considered as derived from marsh gas by the substitution of the hydrogen by the three univalent radicals:

$$\text{HO, COOH, and} \quad \text{COOH}-\overset{\displaystyle H}{\underset{\displaystyle OH}{\overset{|}{\underset{|}{C}}}}-,$$

consequently it should manifest rotatory power, and indeed this is just what it does. Moreover, an examination of the formula shows that the last of the substituted groups is identical with the grouping of the entire remainder of the compound; we have to deal, therefore, with the second class of exceptions to the first general principle. Two arrangements of an inverse symmetry being possible in this grouping, if the two groups combined with one another are identical and superposable their effect upon the polarized light will be added—this is what takes place with the active acid; if, on the contrary, the combined groups have an inverse symmetry they will exactly neutralize one another and we will have the inactive tartaric acid. This reasoning applies to the derivatives of tartaric acid, and in particular to erythrite. As yet, however, only the inactive erythrite is known; it may be that the active erythrite is not a stable body.

Amylic Group. The active amyl alcohol has the formula:

$$\text{CH}_3-\overset{\displaystyle C_2H_5}{\underset{\displaystyle H}{\overset{|}{\underset{|}{C}}}}-\text{CH}_2\text{OH}$$

Its rotatory power can be foreseen from its formula in the same manner as that of the preceding bodies. This substance gives a very numerous series of derivatives which show the rotatory power, and this characteristic is shown in their formulas. As examples we may cite all of the ethers of amyl alcohol, and the acid derived from it, valeric acid:

$$\text{CH}_3-\overset{\displaystyle C_2H_5}{\underset{\displaystyle H}{\overset{|}{\underset{|}{C}}}}-\text{COOH}$$

the valerates, the valeric ethers, amylamine and nearly all of the hydrocarbons containing the radical amyl, such as the ethylamyl, diamyl, etc.   It is no longer the same with the hydride of amyl:

$$CH_3 - \underset{\underset{H}{|}}{\overset{\overset{C_2H_5}{|}}{C}} - CH_3$$

We see in fact, that it contains two methyl groups united to the same carbon; this body is, indeed, inactive.

This fact proves that the presence of the amyl radical does not necessitate the rotatory power in all of its combinations.

Mr. Würtz has shown that the caproic acid derived from the active amyl cyanide has rotatory power.   If we compare this acid with the active valeric acid, the formula of which has already been given, we see that it is derived from amyl alcohol just as valeric acid is derived from the secondary butyl alcohol of Mr. de Luynes.   We are able to conclude empirically, therefore, that this last alcohol is active; we arrive directly at the same result by applying the first general principle to the formula of this secondary alcohol which is:

$$CH_3 - \underset{\underset{H}{|}}{\overset{\overset{C_2H_5}{|}}{C}} - OH$$

The author occupies himself with the preparation of many derivatives of this group in order to verify their action upon polarized light.

The Sugar Group.   The general constitution of the sugars is known, but their exact formulas have not yet been given; we must therefore confine ourselves to the prediction of facts based upon the general formulas.

In all the sugars we usually find a carbon united with hydrogen, with hydroxyl, and with two complex radicals; if the radicals are different, as very generally happens, the sugar in question should be active.   It has been observed, in fact, that most sugars possess rotatory power.

The sugars are naturally divided into hexatomic alcohols, such as mannite, and into glucoses.   Let us consider the normal hexatomic alcohol

$$CH_2\,OH\ CHOH\ CHOH\ CHOH - \underset{\underset{OH}{|}}{\overset{\overset{H}{|}}{C}} - CH_2\,OH;$$

we see that each of the four central carbon atoms possesses the characteristics of rotatory power, although in the formula above given this is indicated with the fifth carbon atom only.

If the only cause of the asymmetry of this molecule were the mode of arrangement of the radicals surrounding a single one of these four carbons, we should have a lævo and a dextro body only; but as four similar groupings exist there will be as many isomers as one can imagine combinations among these groupings. This is a repetition of the facts which we have already met with in tartaric acid, but in this case all of the isomers are not yet known.

It should be observed that the groups immediately surrounding the central carbon atoms in the above formula are the same, that is to say, the radicals with which they are combined are either identical such as H, and OH, or they differ but slightly in their most remote parts; if then the similar groupings give rise to rotatory power in contrary directions, we see that they will compensate one another, or nearly so; so that the rotatory power of the whole molecule will be nothing, or very slight. This is perhaps the explanation of the fact that the rotatory power of mannite, dulcite, and their hexanitrate, and hexa-acetate is so much reduced.

This supposition which, however, is independent of the general theory, finds confirmation in the fact that the glucoses have a much greater rotatory power; now the glucoses have an aldehydic or a ketonic function; let us consider the normal aldehydic glucose:

$$CH_2\ OH\ CHOH\ CHOH\ CHOH-\overset{\displaystyle H}{\underset{\displaystyle HO}{|}}\overset{|}{\underset{|}{C}}-COH:$$

we see that the asymmetric grouping which surrounds the fifth carbon is completely different from all of the others, and there is no longer any reason that its effect upon polarized light should be compensated by that of the neighboring groups. We understand now how the hydrogenation of very active glucoses may give hexatomic alcohols almost destitute of rotatory power.

Fatty Bodies with Two Free Valences. We have not yet considered active unsaturated bodies, for we do not include in this class bodies which are formed by the substitution of an active radical in an unsaturated inactive body, such as, for example, allyl valerate.

We have but to examine the case where the double linking of the unsaturated body is caused by the disappearance of some of the radicals, the asymmetrical grouping of which caused the rotatory power in the corresponding saturated body.

Since all the substances with two free valences are derived from ethylene, it is to this latter we must, if possible, apply the general principles which we have previously employed. We shall put aside the case where the four atoms of hydrogen do not have fixed positions with regard to one another, for it is clear that in such a case their substitution would not furnish asymmetric bodies. If, on the contrary, these relative positions are fixed, we can apply to ethylene the same reasoning that was applied to marsh gas.

If the four atoms of hydrogen lie in the same plane, which is a possible case of equilibrium, there will be no active trisubstitution derivatives; however, we do not know examples of well studied bodies derived from ethylene by three different substitutions, and we are therefore unable to solve this question at present.

As to the second general principle, it is not applicable to ethylene, for the formula $CH_2{=}CH_2$ shows that by two different substitutions chemically different isomers [4] are obtained. This is not opposed to the atoms being in the same plane, in which case the derivatives formed by two substitutions will be inactive. In any other case, to explain the isomerism of the ethylene derivatives, we must suppose the hydrogen atoms to be at the angles of a hemihedral quadratic pyramid [5] superposable upon its image $\frac{P}{2}$, and we should obtain by two substitutions two isomers, one of which would be symmetrical [6] and the other unsymmetrical. These isomers will both be symmetrical if the two substituted radicals are the same, as happens in the case of maleïc and fumaric acids. [7] Hence it is sufficient for the optical study of two bisubstitution derivatives, such as the amylene of active amyl alcohol $CH_2{=}C\,{}^{CH_3}_{C_2H_5}$, and its isomer $CH_3CH{=}CH{-}C_2H_5$, to decide whether the four hydrogen atoms are in the same plane or not.

---

[4] [The two "chemically different" isomers would be $CXY{=}CH_2$ and $CHX{=}CHY$.—O.T.B.]

[5] [Hemihedral quadratic pyramid: a figure obtained if the plane of one CH_2 group of ethylene is rotated to a position perpendicular to the plane of the other CH_2 group.—O.T.B.]

[6] [$CXY{=}CH_2$ would be symmetrical.—O.T.B.]

[7] [Le Bel assumes that the formulas for maleic and fumaric acid are $CHCO_2H{=}CHCO_2H$ and $CH_2{=}C(CO_2H)_2$. Van't Hoff did not even consider the latter a possibility (see above, p. 156), presumably because Kekulé had rejected the formula on chemical grounds.—O.T.B.]

Aromatic series.[8] All chemists agree in the opinion that the atoms of hydrogen in benzene occupy fixed positions; we can no longer consider, as we did in the case of the saturated bodies, a part of the benzene molecule as a single material point; but we make use of this restrictive hypothesis again in the case of the radicals or groups which replace hydrogen in benzene. The geometrical hypotheses which account for the isomerism of the aromatic series have already been discussed elsewhere; they assume that the six atoms of hydrogen are situated at the six equal angles of a rhombohedron, or perhaps at those of a right prism (pyramid) with an equilateral triangular base. Simple geometrical reasoning shows that in either case by two different substitutions there are obtained one asymmetrical and two different symmetrical isomers; the existence of an active cymene[9] which has been described confirms these hypotheses, which we will not discuss farther.

Without ascribing to the atoms of hydrogen in benzene any particular grouping, we can apply the first general principle to any three atoms of hydrogen whatever, provided that they do not occupy a plane of symmetry of the whole molecule. Hence it follows that we shall meet with active bodies whenever at least three atoms of hydrogen are replaced by different radicals. We find this assumption realized in a large number of substances in the camphor series. (See for their formulas the work of Mr. Kekulé, Bull. Soc. chim., t. XX. 1873, p. 558.) Camphor, for example, is derived from benzene by the substitution of hydrogen by the following groups:

$$CH_3, \begin{bmatrix} C_3H_7 \\ H \end{bmatrix}'', O'', H_2, \text{ and } H_2 ;$$

three of them are different and the two others are not able to re-establish the symmetry; it has been proved in fact that all of these bodies are active.

---

[8] [The argument with regard to the aromatic series is confusing for two reasons:
  (a) le Bel switches his discussion from a solid model to "Mr. Kekulé's hexagon";
  (b) the argument is shifted from benzene substitution compounds derived from C_6H_6 to derivatives of cyclohexane C_6H_{12}.
Benzene substitution products cannot be optically active as all groups are in the plane of the benzene ring (with the exception of cases where one or more of the substituted groups are asymmetric).—O.T.B.]

[9] [The active cymene must be *m*-cymene, i.e. 3-isopropyl methylcyclohexane. The isomeric inactive *p*-cymene is mentioned two paragraphs below.—O.T.B.]

The case is not the same for the spirit of turpentine; we know that this is derived, as is also the camphor series, from para-cymene, in which the radicals methyl and propyl occupy positions 1 and 4 of Mr. Kekulé's hexagon, that is to say in a plane of symmetry of benzene, and this is the reason why cymene is inactive.

Now the spirit of turpentine is derived from cymene by the substitution of two H_2 groups for two atoms of hydrogen; if these occupy the positions 2 and 6 or 3 and 5, symmetrical with regard to the plane of symmetry passing through 1 and 4, we shall have inactive isomers; on the other hand we shall have active isomers (terebenthene and camphene) if they occupy positions not symmetrical to one another, as 2 and 5 or 2 and 3; we might apply the same reasoning to the other isomers of terebenthene, (for the formulas of these see the memoir of Mr. Oppenheim, loc. cit. p. 560).

It is possible that camphoric acid, the constitution of which is not yet fully established, comes under the preceding case.

Quinnic acid which is equally active is derived from benzene by a different but insufficiently understood mode of substitution; we shall not, therefore, discuss it here.

We see what interest is attached to the study of active aromatic compounds, and how necessary it is that chemists who are dealing with bi- and trisubstitution products of benzene capable of being active should attempt the separation of their dextro- and lævorotatory isomers. We shall proceed to show that bodies obtained by synthesis consist, in fact, of equal proportions of these isomers.

Theorem. When an asymmetric body is formed in a reaction where there are present originally only symmetrical bodies, the two isomers of inverse symmetry will be formed in equal quantities.

We know that the general principle of the calculation of probabilities consists in this:

When any phenomenon whatever can take place in two ways only, and there is no reason why it should take place in one of the ways in preference to the other, if the phenomenon has taken place m times in one manner and m' times in the other manner the ratio $\frac{m}{m'}$, approaches unity as the sum $m + m'$ approaches infinity.

When an asymmetric body has been formed by substitution from a symmetric one, the asymmetry has been introduced by one of the substitutions which has taken place; let us consider this point carefully. The radical or the atom the substitution of which introduced the asymmetry had formerly a homologue which was symmetrical to it by its connection with a point or a plane of symmetry; these radicals being in similar dynamic and geometrical conditions, if m and m' represent the number of times that each one of them is substituted, $\dfrac{m'}{m}$ ought to approach unity as the number of these substitutions grows beyond a measurable limit.

Now if the substitution of one of these similar radicals produces a dextro-body then the other will produce the lævo-body, both will in consequence be formed in equal proportions.

It is the same for asymmetric bodies formed by addition; indeed the body which destroys the symmetry of a symmetrical molecule by adding itself to it, would be able to occupy an identical place situated on the other side of the point or plane of symmetry; the preceding reasoning therefore can be applied equally well to this case.

This is not necessarily true of asymmetric bodies formed in the presence of other active bodies, or traversed by circularly polarized light, or, in short, when submitted to any cause whatever which favors the formation of one of the asymmetric isomers. Such conditions are exceptional; and generally in the case of bodies prepared synthetically those which are active will escape the observation of the chemist unless he endeavors to separate the mixed isomeric products, the combined action of which upon polarized light is neutral.

We have a striking example of this in tartaric acid, for neither the dextro- nor the lævo-tartaric acid has ever been obtained directly by synthesis, but the inactive racemic acid which is a combination of equal parts of the dextro and lævo acids, is always obtained.

Epilogue

By 1858 a major chapter in the valence story had been completed: the *fact* of valence, of a saturation-combining capacity, had been established, and its magnitude in the case of a considerable number of elements was known. The concept, however, was accepted at a heavy cost. Its acceptance demanded the renunciation of the only mechanism by which atoms could be considered to be held together. Berzelius' electrochemical conception fell into disrepute. Its place was taken by a picture of the atom as a sphere with a fixed number of knobs or hooks at which combination had to take place. For reasons unknown, atoms combined and tended to utilize all their combining hooks. The number of hooks was a property of the element which was as characteristic as was its atomic weight, and of equally mysterious origin.

The beginnings of stereochemistry were hardly more auspicious. The tetrahedral distribution of the valences of carbon was a necessary assumption to explain isomerism. Though there was some logic to the correlation of a tetrahedron with the number four, no successful general correlation between valence and stereochemistry was forthcoming for over half a century. Chemistry became empirical. Success could be achieved without asking the question, "Why?" Synthetic organic chemistry flourished, while theoretical chemistry waned.

Two men, Butlerov and Cannizzaro, deserve the major credit for forcefully presenting to their chemical colleagues the implications of the chemical achievements of the previous fifty years. A. M. Butlerov, professor of chemistry at the University of Kazan, visited Germany and France in 1857 and became personally acquainted with Kekulé and Couper. He was probably the first to sense the full implications and potentialities of the structural theory of organic chemistry. He calculated the number of isomers of a given molecular formula, and used the theory as a guide to the synthesis of important classes of organic compounds.[1] He used the term "chemical structure" to designate "the type and manner of the mutual binding of the atoms in a compound substance" and

---

[1] See H. M. Leicester, *J. chem. Educ.*, *36*, 328 (1959).

insisted, contrary to the followers of the type theory, that there was only one structure for each compound. In 1861, in his speech to the Speyer meeting of German naturalists, during which he introduced these ideas, he also stated that they were all implicit in Couper's papers of 1858.[2] In subsequent years his contribution was to draw the full consequences of Kekulé's and Couper's theories. Butlerov suggested, for instance, one of the early and essentially correct explanations of tautomerism.

Stanislao Cannizzaro (1826–1910), professor of chemistry at Genoa, published in 1858 a summary of the implications of the hypothesis of his countryman, Amedeo Avogadro. Using the hypothesis as his fundamental guiding principle, he derived its consequences, including the diatomicity of the common gases and a consistent set of atomic weights. The paper was ignored, as Avogadro's had been earlier. Cannizzaro came to the Karlsruhe Chemical Congress of 1860 determined to present his views. The Congress had been called by Kekulé and others for the express purpose of clarifying the confusion resultant on the use of the many systems of atomic weights. Cannizzaro spoke at several sessions and gave an impassioned speech at the conclusion of the conference. The members were not convinced. On leaving they were handed a reprint of Cannizzaro's article, and on their way home some of them suddenly discovered the only possible solution to their difficulties. Among these was Lothar Meyer, who helped see to it that the lesson was learned. Within a few years textbooks and articles finally switched to the viewpoint espoused by Cannizzaro.

Much, however, remained to be accomplished. In 1865 Kekulé supplied a structural explanation for benzene compounds, suggesting the hexagonal arrangement of the six carbon atoms. On the other hand, he fought bitterly for years against the view of a variable valence for elements, a view which had the backing of Frankland, Couper, Wurtz and Naquet. In this matter, Kekulé was wrong, and the possibility of multiple characteristic valences of a given element became a further fact requiring explanation.

Valence was recognized as a periodic property by Mendeleev, and was used in his construction of the periodic table in 1869; yet this development threw no new light on the origin or character of valence forces. For that, chemists had to await the elucidation of atomic structure.

In the years that followed, one other broad area of valence problems was brought to the same state of partial completion.

---

[2] A. M. Butlerov, *Zeitschrift für Chemie*, **4**, 549 (1861).

The theories of 1858 could help but little in the understanding of so-called "molecular" or "complex" compounds. No doctrine of fixed combining capacity could account for the series of stable substances:

$$CoCl_3.6NH_3$$
$$CoCl_3.5NH_3$$
$$CoCl_3.4NH_3$$
$$CoCl_3.3NH_3$$

Berzelius, Graham, Jørgensen and others had attempted explanations, but none was general enough to account for the body of known material. In a flash of insight, Alfred Werner (1866–1919) in 1891 recognized the pattern underlying the formulas. He proposed that the central metal atom could attach to itself in a first or inner sphere a fixed number (most commonly 6 or 4) of atoms or groups, irrespective of whether these were univalent atoms or groups, or molecules stable in the absence of such a combination. This fixed number he called the coordination number. The molecule might in addition contain further atoms or groups (but not stable molecules), less strongly attached, in a second sphere. In the case of the cobaltic salts, the coordination number was six; Werner's formulation of the substances mentioned above being:

$$[Co(NH_3)_6] \quad Cl_3$$
$$[Co(NH_3)_5Cl] \quad Cl_2$$
$$[Co(NH_3)_4Cl_2]Cl$$
$$[Co(NH_3)_3Cl_3].$$

Only the chlorine appearing outside the inner sphere, represented by the square brackets, could be precipitated with silver nitrate solution or could contribute to the solution's conductance. The last substance did not conduct electricity at all. For every univalent group replacing a neutral molecule in the inner sphere, the electrovalence of the complex is reduced by one.

Werner further suggested spatial positions for the coordinated groups, an octahedron for coordination number 6, a square or tetrahedron (distinguishable by types and number of isomers) if the number was 4.

It looked for a while as if there were two quite independent valence patterns, one for the compounds of carbon and the other for the rest of chemistry. Werner, however, insisted that the structural theory of organic chemistry was a special case of coordination theory, the carbon atom having a valence equal to its coordination number. The two theories did not find a common footing until the advent of electronic valence theories.

The impetus for the next advance came from physics. The atoms were discovered not to be simple. The atomic nature of electricity was deduced from Faraday's laws of electrolysis by G. Johnstone Stoney in 1874 and by Helmholtz in 1881; the electron was discovered in 1897 by J. J. Thomson in electric discharges. Electrons were soon realized to be constituents of all matter. Thomson conceived of the electrons in an atom as embedded in a sphere of uniform positive electrification, but such a model, though possibly stable, could not account for the large angle deflections of α-particles bombarding a thin gold foil, as observed by Rutherford's students, Geiger and Marsden. Earlier results had shown that the number of electrons in an atom equaled about half the atomic weight. Rutherford now deduced that only a single massive positive nucleus could cause such deflections, the positive charge on the nucleus equaling numerically the sum of the charges on the electrons.

By 1911, van den Broek had proposed that different elements were characterized by different integral nuclear charges, and that every charge from one to the largest known would correspond to a separate element. The suggestion gained significance from studies of radioactive transformations, and was placed on a secure footing by Moseley's work with X-ray spectra in 1913.

Rutherford's model was unstable. One could consider the electrons to rotate around the nucleus but, as Niels Bohr pointed out,[3] rotating charged particles cannot be likened to planets; in rotating, they must radiate energy, and hence spiral into the nucleus. Since atoms clearly neither collapsed nor radiated a continuous range of wave lengths, something was wrong.

Because a static system of charge centers was quite unmanageable theoretically, Bohr borrowed from the newer physics one principle to be applied to the Rutherford model. Basing himself on Planck's quantum hypothesis, he proposed that electrons could only exist in a certain limited number of orbits. When they were rotating in these orbits, no energy was released, radiation being emitted only when an electron changed orbits. The frequency of the radiation emitted is related to the orbital energies E_1 and E_2 by the expression $\nu = (E_1 - E_2)/h$, where h is Planck's constant. According to Bohr, only a certain small number of electrons could be accommodated in each shell, and the shell conception gave impetus to attempts to correlate chemical periodicity with atomic structure.

The inert gases were immediately regarded as points of departure

---

[3] N. Bohr, *Phil. Mag.*, *26*, 476 (1913).

for this investigation. Their numbers of electrons had to constitute a particularly stable set, and the differences between them followed an interesting pattern: He 2, Ne 10, Ar 18, Kr 36, Xe 54, Rn 86, with increments of 8, 8, 18, 18, 32, which are twice the squares of whole numbers, $2n^2$. Furthermore, atoms with the atomic number one greater than the inert gases formed a family of similar elements, the alkali metals, while other families showed similar relationships. It was at first thought that each shell fills completely before the next one is begun, but C. R. Bury[4] on the basis of chemical considerations, and Bohr on spectral evidence, concluded that such a view was untenable. Inner shells often were only partially filled, new shells begun, and subsequently the inner shells were completed. The electronic assignments for the inert gases then became:

> He 2,
> Ne 2, 8
> Ar 2, 8, 8
> Kr 2, 8, 18, 8
> Xe 2, 8, 18, 18, 8
> Rn 2, 8, 18, 32, 18, 8

no outer shell being able to hold more than eight electrons.

But some years before this refinement, electronic interpretations of valence were proposed, first tentatively by Thomson, Ramsey and others, then in concrete form by W. Kossel, G. N. Lewis and I. Langmuir. Walter Kossel (1888–   )[5] pointed to the fact that metals which combine with non-metals to form strongly ionizing salts have atomic numbers just above those of the inert gases, while the non-metals with which they combine lack one or two electrons relative to the inert gas structures. By a simple transfer of electrons, both combining atoms could attain an inert gas configuration, the atoms in the process becoming positively and negatively charged. Kossel realized that this theory was limited, since it had no explanation for compounds formed between pairs of atoms where the number of electrons of both atoms was just below that of an inert gas. The common gases, oxygen, nitrogen and chlorine, are examples. Nor could he account for the great difference in properties between ionizing and non-ionizing materials, known since the time of Berzelius and re-emphasized by the work of Arrhenius in 1887.

---

[4] C. R. Bury, *Journal of the American Chemical Society*, **43**, 1602 (1921).

[5] W. Kossel, *Annalen der Physik*, **49**, 229 (1916).

Gilbert Newton Lewis (1875–1946) in the same year (1916) supplied an answer.[6] His paper begins by pointing out the need to substitute for the "conventional classification of chemical substances, as inorganic or organic, the more general classification which distinguishes between polar and non-polar substances." He proceeds to demonstrate the continuous gradation in properties from completely polar to non-polar compounds, thus making it unlikely that a sharp break separates the two. Building on Abegg's law that the sum of maximum positive and negative valences of the elements tends to be eight, and is never more than eight (positive valence being the valence exhibited toward non-metals, negative valence that exhibited toward metals or hydrogen), Lewis constructs a cubic model of the atom, electrons in the outer shell occupying corners of the cube and obeying the following postulates:

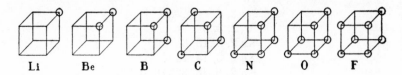

1. In every atom is an essential *kernel* which remains unaltered in all ordinary chemical changes and which possesses an excess of positive charges corresponding in number to the ordinal number of the group in the periodic table to which the element belongs.
2. The atom is composed of the kernel and an *outer atom* or *shell*, which, in the case of the neutral atom, contains negative electrons equal in number to the excess of positive charges of the kernel, but the number of electrons in the shell may vary during chemical change between 0 and 8.
3. The atom tends to hold an even number of electrons in the shell, and especially to hold eight electrons which are normally arranged symmetrically at the eight corners of a cube.
4. Two atomic shells are mutually interpenetrable.
5. Electrons may ordinarily pass with readiness from one position in the outer shell to another. Nevertheless, they are held in position by more or less rigid constraints, and these positions and the magnitude of the constraints are determined by the nature of the atom and of such other atoms as are combined with it.
6. Electric forces between particles which are very close together do not obey the simple law of inverse squares, which holds at greater distances.

In a footnote, Lewis comments that his cubical diagrams date from a memorandum of March 28, 1902, together with notes concerning different types of compounds, and the relationship between

---

[6] G. N. Lewis, *J. Amer. chem. Soc.*, *38*, 762–785 (1916).

symmetrical structure and atomic volume. The two most important postulates are the even-number rule, and the assumption that the outer shells of two atoms are mutually interpenetrable. Together, they lead to a new kind of bond, involving the sharing of an electron pair, and represented by the sharing of an edge between the two cubes. Lewis emphasizes that sharing does not necessarily mean equal sharing, thus leading to the concept of a polar covalent bond.

The Lewis model has become so famous and has for years been used so mechanically that some of the considerations underlying it are here presented. They demonstrate how deeply Lewis was concerned with the underlying physical cause of valence rather than with a simple rule of thumb. He further points up an operational difficulty in Bohr's atomic model: if it gives no information as to the electron's movement within an orbit, we have no business postulating its movement. Furthermore, electrons "orbiting" around a nucleus could not possibly explain directed valences. Lewis, therefore, proposed a static model, confident that theoretical chemistry would somehow, some day, confirm it:[7]

Now there are only two ways in which one body can be held by another. It may, owing to a force of attraction, be drawn toward the second body until this force is gradually offset by a more rapidly increasing force of repulsion. In this case it comes to rest at a point where the net attraction or repulsion is zero, and is therefore in a condition of constraint with respect to any motion along the line joining the two centers; for if the distance between the two bodies is diminished they repel one another, while if the distance is increased they are attracted toward one another. An example of this type is a body attracted toward the earth but resting upon an elastic substance where the attractive force of gravity is offset by the repulsive force which we happen to call elastic; but it would be a mistake to consider the forces of elasticity to be different in character from other known forces. Indeed it is evident that just as we have the law of universal attraction between particles at great distances, so *at small distances* we have the equally universal *law of repulsion*.

The other way in which one body may hold another is that in which the planets are held by the sun, and this is the way that in some current theories of atomic structure the electrons are supposed to be held by the atom. Such an assumption seems inadequate to explain even the simplest chemical properties of the atom, and I imagine it has been introduced only for the sake of maintaining the laws of electromagnetics which are known to be valid at large distances. The fact is, however, that in the more prominent of these theories even this questionable advantage disappears, for the common laws of electricity are not preserved. The most interesting and suggestive of these theories is the one proposed by Bohr and based upon Planck's quantum theory. Planck in his elementary oscillator which maintains its motion at the absolute zero, and Bohr in his electron moving in a fixed orbit, have invented systems containing electrons of which the motion

[7] G. N. Lewis, *loc. cit.*

produces no effect upon external charges. Now this is not only inconsistent with the accepted laws of electromagnetics but, I may add, is logically objectionable, for that state of motion which produces no physical effect whatsoever may better be called a state of rest.

Indeed, it seems hardly likely that much progress can be made in the solution of the difficult problems relating to chemical combination by assigning in advance definite laws of force between the positive and negative constituents of an atom, and then on the basis of these laws building up mechanical models of the atom. We must first of all, from a study of chemical phenomena, learn the structure and the arrangement of the atoms, and if we find it necessary to alter the law of force acting between charged particles at small distances, even to the extent of changing the sign of that force, it will not be the first time in the history of science that an increase in the range of observational material has required a modification of generalizations based upon a smaller field of observation. Indeed in the present case, entirely aside from any chemical reasons, a study of the mathematical theory of the electron leads, I believe, irresistibly to the conclusion that Coulomb's law of inverse squares must fail at small distances.

Lewis now proposes to represent the atomic *kernels* by the usual chemical symbols for the elements, and the outer shell electrons by dots. Iodine becomes $:\overset{\cdots}{\underset{\cdots}{I}}:\overset{\cdots}{\underset{\cdots}{I}}:$, and the sulfate ion becomes

$$:\overset{\cdots}{\underset{\cdots}{O}}:$$
$$:\overset{\cdots}{\underset{\cdots}{O}}:\overset{\cdots}{\underset{\cdots}{S}}:\overset{\cdots}{\underset{\cdots}{O}}:,$$
$$:\overset{\cdots}{\underset{\cdots}{O}}:$$

where each atom attains an inert gas shell of eight electrons. Double bonds as in ethylene can be represented by the sharing of a face of a cube, but triple bonds require a further extension. Emphasizing the significance of electron pairs, he suggests that these are somehow drawn together by forces as yet unknown. The four pairs around the central atom in a compound of carbon occupy the midpoints of four edges of the cube. The edges chosen are those that maximize the distances between electron pairs. The pairs thus occupy the corners of a tetrahedron, and acetylene is formed by the sharing of a face between two such tetrahedra.

One suggestion in the Lewis article threw new light on Werner's coordination compounds. He proposed that electron pair bonds could be formed between atoms, one of which supplied both electrons. Thus the formation of ammonium chloride from ammonia and hydrogen chloride could be conceived as the addition of a proton to the unshared electron pair of ammonia:

$$H \qquad\qquad\qquad H \quad\oplus\qquad \ominus$$
$$H:\overset{\cdots}{N}:+H:\overset{\cdots}{\underset{\cdots}{Cl}}: \rightarrow H:\overset{\cdots}{N}:H \quad :\overset{\cdots}{\underset{\cdots}{Cl}}:$$
$$\overset{}{H} \qquad\qquad\qquad\quad \overset{}{H}$$

The chloride ion "is not attached directly to the nitrogen but is held simply through electric forces by the ammonium ion." The two valence spheres of Werner's complexes thus had a simple explanation. The inner valences were electron pair bonds often formed by the "donor-acceptor" process. The outer valences were electrovalent in character.

Lewis' *Valence and the Structure of Atoms and Molecules,* published in 1923, developed these ideas in considerable detail. In the intervening years he had become even more convinced of the significance of the pairing of electrons. "There is nothing in the known laws of electric force, nor is there anything in the quantum theory of atomic structure, as far as it has yet been developed, to account for such pairing. . . . The explanation of this phenomenon must be regarded as one of the most important outstanding problems of quantum theory."[8] Lewis was not mistaken. Two years after his book was written, one of the basic principles of modern valence theory, the Pauli exclusion principle, was enunciated, and has remained one of the cornerstones of wave mechanics. Originally stated in the form that no two electrons in an atom can have the same four quantum numbers, it may be expressed as the principle that not more than two electrons in an atom or molecule can occupy the same orbital or region of space.

The Lewis theory was a monumental achievement; yet it still left the fundamental questions unanswered. "Why do stable electron groupings in atoms exist?" "Why do atoms form molecules?" "Why is there a limit to their combining capacity?" The statement that atoms tend to attain inert gas configurations only begs the question as to why these are particularly stable. Only in one area did Lewis seem to arrive at an almost final answer. The stereochemistry of covalent bonds is determined by the mutual repulsion of electron pairs. This view in its generalized form was revived by Nevil Vincent Sidgwick in 1940,[9] but was mainly ignored. It was recently proposed again by Nyholm and Gillespie,[10] and now seems to be recognized as one of the great simplifying generalizations (outside of the transition metals and rare-earth elements) emerging out of quantum theory.

The lines between atoms in organic formulas could only be

---

[8] G. N. Lewis, *Valence and the Structure of Atoms and Molecules* (New York: Chemical Catalog Company, 1923), pp. 57–58.

[9] N. V. Sidgwick and H. M. Powell, *Proceedings of the Royal Society, A176,* 153 (1940).

[10] R. S. Nyholm and R. J. Gillespie, *Progress in Stereochemistry, 2,* 261 (1958).

single, double, or triple. When electrons were introduced into formulas, each line was replaced by an electron pair. The electron pairs, according to the chemical theories of the time, were static. Such conceptions were difficult to reconcile with what the physicist knew about electrons and what the organic chemist was beginning to suspect about chemical bonds. The physicist's discoveries about the wave nature of electrons and his realization of the probabilistic character of scientific knowledge led to the development of wave mechanics. When applied to chemistry, one of the most useful aspects was the concept of quantum-mechanical resonance as applied to the successful elucidation of the nature of the covalent bond and to the multicentered bonds of benzene and related compounds. The organic chemist, also concerned with benzene, was led to formulate an extension of valence theory almost exactly parallel to the wave-mechanical approach.

The fragmentation of the valence line is due in large measure to Friedrich Karl Johannes Thiele[11] (1865–1918). Earlier formulas for unsaturated compounds such as ethylene, C_2H_4, had left residual integral valences unused, thus explaining the reactivity of these compounds. When it was found that residual valences almost invariably occurred in pairs involving adjacent carbon atoms, it was assumed that adjacent free valences satisfied one another. But a doubly linked carbon pair, as in $H_2C{=}CH_2$, suggests a molecule less reactive than a singly bound one, contrary to the facts. Thiele, therefore, proposed that only a part of the valence force was used for the second bond, leaving some free affinity. In systems of alternating single and double bonds, the theory could explain why bromine often adds to the end carbon atoms, since the residual affinities of neighboring atoms could satisfy one another across single bonds:

$$
\begin{array}{ccc}
H & & H \\
| & & | \\
H-C{=}C-C{=}C-H \\
\vdots \quad \vdots\!\!\cdots\!\!\vdots \quad \vdots \\
Br & & Br
\end{array}
$$

In a cyclic system such as benzene, all residual valences could be mutually satisfied, explaining the remarkable inertness of aromatic compounds. In benzene, Thiele proposed a complete redistribution of bonds, leading to a regular hexagon structure:

----

[11] F. K. J. Thiele, *Ann.*, *306*, 87 (1899).

In addition to explaining benzene's lack of reactivity, this formula predicted the correct number of substitutional isomers. Kekulé's oscillating formulas (1872), on the other hand, could explain only the correct isomerism.

The redistribution of integral valences was expressed in a form consonant with electronic structures by Fritz Arndt *et al.* in 1924,[12] and became known as the theory of intermediate stages. To explain the fact that γ-pyrones did not react either as typical unsaturated compounds or as ketones, he wrote the two formulas:

I II

and stated:

> It is to be emphasized that formula II...is certainly not such a clear-cut betaine dipole as formula II would indicate. But with the new views [Zwitterions] according to which no new bond across the ring is involved but all boils down to a shift of electronic orbitals, any intermediate states [*Zwischenstufen*] can be conceived.[13]

Here was expressed the essential chemical basis of modern resonance theory. When energies of the separate extreme forms are calculated and introduced into wave-mechanical equations, the

---

[12] F. Arndt, E. Scholz and F. Nachtwey, *Ber.*, **57**, 1903 (1924).
[13] Ref. 12, p. 1906. For translation, see E. Campaigne, *J. chem. Educ.*, **36**, 337 (1959).

state of lowest energy of the system turns out to be one where positions of nuclei and distributions of electrons are intermediate between those of the two formulas. Wave-mechanical calculations were carried out by Hückel in 1932[14] and by Pauling and Wheland in 1933,[15] confirming the theory and giving it a quantitative framework. Beginning in 1929, Ingold and his co-workers developed and applied the theory of resonance to explain many areas of organic chemistry, while Pauling has done the same for inorganic chemistry.[16] The theory has become one of the fundamental conceptual pillars of chemistry.[17]

The province of valence theory is by no means fully charted. On the contrary, in recent years it has once again attracted many explorers. It is one of the busiest regions of the science of chemistry. Wave mechanics, once the preserve of a few mathematical physicists, has become accessible to many; a number of relatively painless routes into its rugged territory have been discovered. Particularly, inorganic chemistry has been revitalized by the newer wavemechanical valence theories, coupled with the application of the physico-chemical methods of investigation that have proved so eminently successful in the elucidation of organic structures and mechanisms. Happily, a sufficient number of baffling problems remain to presage further transformations in this field of study.[18]

[14] E. Hückel, *Zeitschrift für Physik*, *70*, 204 (1931); *72*, 310 (1931); *76*, 628 (1932).

[15] L. Pauling and G. W. Wheland, *Journal of chemical Physics*, *1*, 362 (1933).

[16] See C. K. Ingold, *Structure and Mechanism in Organic Chemistry*, Ithaca, Cornell Univeristy Press, 1953; L. Pauling, *The Nature of the Chemical Bond*, 3rd edn., Ithaca, Cornell University Press, 1960.

[17] See G. W. Wheland, *Resonance in Organic Chemistry*, New York, John Wiley & Sons, 1955.

[18] For further discussions of the present state of valence theory, see, for instance, E. Cartmell and G. W. A. Fowles, *Valency and Molecular Structure*, New York, Academic Press, 2nd Ed., 1961; and C. A. Coulson, *Valence*, New York, Oxford University Press, 1952.

Index